Innovation in manufacturing through digital technologies and applications:
Thoughts and Reflections on Industry 4.0.

Innovation in manufacturing through digital technologies and applications: Thoughts and Reflections on Industry 4.0.

Edited by:

Dr. Adel Aneiba, Prof. Cham Athwal and Prof. Hanifa Shah
School of Computing and Digital Technology,
Birmingham City University, Birmingham, UK.

Series Editors:

Prof. Gareth Neighbour and Prof. Andrew Aftelak

Printed by: Belmont Press

Published by:

 BIRMINGHAM CITY University

Special Publication

ISBN: 978-1-5272-2983-9

A Catalogue record for this book is available from the British Library

First printed in 2018 by Belmont Press

Published by Birmingham City University, University House, Birmingham B5 5JU

Printed in the United Kingdom

SERIES EDITORS' INTRODUCTION

We are delighted to present this special volume dedicated to Industry 4.0 supported by a dedicated conference. We are very grateful to the editors and authors who have worked tirelessly to produce the book ready to launch at the conference in October 2018. Industry 4.0, although based on long-standing principles in manufacturing, has really come to the fore through the power of computing and data handling and whilst challenges remain, the use of Industry 4.0 will undoubtedly increase competitiveness and the ability to manufacture minimising cost and waste.

The initial 'Thoughts and Reflections' book concerning the use of magnesium was conceived through a need to raise the profile of magnesium and dispel some of the myths especially regarding its flammability. It also served as a basis to showcase strengths of the partnership working with the world leading organisation Meridian as well as other stakeholders. Importantly, the book allowed colleagues working in various areas to explore some of the academic underpinning knowledge and express them as thoughts and reflections for the wider academic community. This is very much as the heart of the vision and ethos of the faculty at Birmingham City University to share with a wider audience world leading activity in a more focussed and open form of a book. It is pleasing to see that the first book was very well received... so much in fact that this second book has been developed focussing on Industry 4.0. Indeed, we are pleased to announce we will be developing a series of texts based on the concept of "Thoughts and Reflections" with invited editors for each volume. At present the intention is to present a first series of volumes as outlined below.

- Advanced Technologies & Manufacturing
- Big Data
- Connectivity and 5G
- Cyber Security
- Digital Construction
- Future Living and Socio-Technical Systems (incorporating smart cities)
- Healthy Environments and Communities
- Machine Learning and Artificial Intelligence
- The Low Carbon Economy (including Autonomous Vehicles, Fuel Cells and Energy)

This series will seek to record emerging gaps and allow a wider community to challenge existing thinking in an area. Many of these areas have under-developed aspects especially at the periphery, for example how does advanced technologies such as autonomous vehicles change town planning and the use of facilities in future cities? Or how does digital construction create a less wasteful society with more effective on-site manufacturing of civil engineering structures? There are many similar questions to which we hope to provide some answers. We welcome contributions from all and in particular industrial support associated with each volume. Equally, ideas for new volumes in the "Thoughts and Reflections" series are similarly welcome.

Prof. Gareth Neighbour

Prof. Andrew Aftelak

Foreword

It is predicted that by 2050, more than 70% of the global population will live in cities with projections of 80% of Gross Domestic Product. Analysts are also predicting that the global population will hit 9.7 billion people by 2050, resulting in potential strains on efforts to reduce poverty, inequality and hunger. Set against this background, the digital technologies agenda will be of critical importance; it will be the responsibility of future generations to understand and implement the ethos and science of 'digital' into their careers and daily lives. Accounting for agricultural production, energy consumption, environmental impact and other variables will be key if we are to sustain social health and well-being. We will need to embrace the new digital age with open arms that can aid in solving the challenges that lie ahead towards the 22nd Century.

Digital technology will become more pivotal to our daily lives than ever before and will also disrupt traditional industries, causing them to become more efficient and further enhance our livelihoods. Digital technology has the potential to increase the social, economic and environmental sustainability of cities across the world and key areas include: data; transport; digital; sensor technology; energy; cyber security; smart cities; connectivity; health; bioenergy; zero/low carbon modern built environment; and even art and design.

One of the key areas of the digital revolution is the term Industry 4.0 – seen by many as the fourth industrial revolution – suggesting that all manufacturing companies will at some point need to take the next technological jump to create more connected, more efficient environments where production efficiency is optimised and controlled via new interventions such as collaborative robots working in parallel with human operators, as well sensor technology and the Internet of Things (IoT). The premise of Industry 4.0 would also imply that these new process advancements are not only most efficient, but also more sustainable with an overall reduced impact on the environment.

With such a large growing population, we will also see unprecedented transport needs – road, air and sea. One of the key areas for manufacturing companies engaged in the transport sector, for example the automotive and aerospace industries, will be of light weighting. As we move towards alternative energy, such as hydrogen and electric/solar power (and perhaps one day, an all-electric/solar powered passenger aircraft) – transport modes will need to become far lighter – and with the circular economy agenda also rapidly growing – we will need to select raw materials that match these key criteria. This is where magnesium will become more prominent than ever within the transport sector, with its excellent light weight, heat dissipation and 100% recyclable properties.

In terms of magnesium metal and digitalisation, we need to distinguish first the range of industries where magnesium is used and second the regional production environments. Further, with the demand of an integrated value chain, magnesium also faces the challenge of having its dominant raw material supply from China. Industry 4.0 technologies are already disrupting and are most likely to shape the future of the automotive value chain. OEMs may become mainly the suppliers of white-label cars to the internet giants. In addition, recent technological advances including sensor technologies, connectivity, augmented reality and machine learning have already impacted the automotive value chain and business models. This is due to their abilities to monitor, track and respond quickly to unexpected events at any point of time across the entire automotive value chain.

To respond to this unique and unprecedented set of global challenges, Birmingham City University has developed significant expertise in the digital arena. This book represents key ideas that are designed to provoke thought around the need for digitalisation within the manufacturing sectors – ensuring that Industry 4.0 progresses to a new age where the impact is reflected on a new world order.

Dr Jamil Ahmed
Makhan Singh
Martin Tauber
Prof. Stephen Brown

Acknowledgments

The Editors would like to express their heartfelt thanks to the many authors who contributed to this volume and colleagues within Birmingham City University (BCU) for their support and engagement. It would be impossible to list all those who have contributed, but the Editors would like to acknowledge the support from the University's senior management most notably Professor Julian Beer, Joanna Birch, Dr Umar Daraz, Professor Melvyn Lees, Professor Keith Osman, Dr Nayan Patel.

Special thanks go to the organisations that have provided support and most notably:

• International Magnesium Association.
• STEAMhouse.

Finally, but not least, the Editors would like to recognise the support of Meridian Lightweight Technologies Inc who made this book possible with their foresight and engagement with BCU, especially Prof. Stephen Brown and Randy Chalmers.

Credits

Cover design by Russ Akers
Creative production by Catherine Davis
Photographed by Nick Robinson

From the "green book" to the "blue book"

"Thoughts and Reflections on the Use of Magnesium" book was published by Birmingham City University in July 2017 as the first in a series of books to be published in association with Meridian Lightweight Technologies UK and the European Committee of the International Magnesium Association. It presented a number of publications focussing on various aspects of the development, processing and application of Magnesium alloys.

Known locally as the "Green Book", the collection of academic papers and industrially based reports and articles covered a range of topics including "Magnesium: A Structural Super Metal"; "Magnesium and Mobility"; "Design Optimisation for Magnesium Parts Used in Automotive Body Structure".

As one may expect, many of the technical chapters addressed the engineering aspects of magnesium relating to its structural properties and potential applications. However, the book differed from other published works by also addressing the attitudes and perceptions of the engineering community towards Magnesium as a useful material: to this end, colleagues from the University's School of Social Psychology joined staff from the Centre of Engineering in compiling the book.

The subject of Women in Engineering was also addressed, as was the University's initiative of involving artists and small businesses in the STEM (Science, Technology, Engineering and Mathematics) agenda as well as the STEAMhouse project which encompasses Science, Technology, Engineering, Art and Mathematics.

The "Green Book" would be compelling reading for anyone interested not only in the design and manufacture of lightweight products but also those with an eye to the future of equality in employment, better utilisation of the Earth's dwindling resources, and the bringing together of scientific and creative communities.

As a result of this work, BCU and its industrial partners have identified several questions and challenges to the academic and research community on how the latest advancements in technology can help engineers to enhance manufacturing performance using Magnesium.

The **blue book** was identified to be the next to be published in this series of publications with its aim to tackle these challenges and raised issues in the Green Book. It explores the potential of Industry 4.0 technologies and applications and identifies the opportunities that Industry 4.0 can offer to the manufacturing sectors and more specifically manufacturing using Magnesium.

Alan Pendry
Prof. Ilias Oraifige

Executive Summary

The rapid pace of developments in digital technologies offers many opportunities to increase the efficiency, flexibility and sophistication of manufacturing processes; including the potential for easier customisation, lower volumes and rapid changeover of products within the same manufacturing cell or line. A number of initiatives on this theme have been proposed around the world to support national industries under names such as Industry 4.0 (Industrie 4.0 in Germany, Made-in-China in China and Made Smarter in the UK).

This book presents an overview of the state of art and upcoming developments in digital technologies pertaining to manufacturing. The starting point is an introduction on Industry 4.0 and its potential for enhancing the manufacturing process. Later on moving to the design of smart (that is digitally driven) business processes which are going to rely on sensing of all relevant parameters, gathering, storing and processing the data from these sensors, using computing power and intelligence at the most appropriate points in the digital workflow including application of edge computing and parallel processing.

A key component of this workflow is the application of Artificial Intelligence and particularly techniques in Machine Learning to derive actionable information from this data; be it real-time automated responses such as actuating transducers or informing human operators to follow specified standard operating procedures or providing management data for operational and strategic planning. Further consideration also needs to be given to the properties and behaviours of particular machines that are controlled and materials that are transformed during the manufacturing process and this is sometimes referred to as Operational Technology (OT) as opposed to IT. The digital capture of these properties and behaviours can then be used to define so-called Cyber Physical Systems.

Given the power of these digital technologies it is of paramount importance that they operate safely and are not vulnerable to malicious interference. Industry 4.0 brings unprecedented cybersecurity challenges to manufacturing and the overall industrial sector and the case is made here that new codes of practice are needed for the combined Information Technology and Operational Technology worlds, but with a framework that should be native to Industry 4.0. Current computing technologies are also able to go in other directions than supporting the digital 'sense to action' process described above. One of these is to use digital technologies to enhance the ability of the human operators who are still essential within the manufacturing process. One such technology, that has recently become accessible for widespread adoption, is Augmented Reality, providing operators with real-time additional information in situ with the machines that they interact with in their workspace in a hands-free mode.

Finally, two linked chapters discuss the specific application of digital technologies to High Pressure Die Casting (HDPC) of Magnesium components. Optimizing the HPDC process is a key task for increasing productivity and reducing defective parts and the first chapter provides an overview of the HPDC process with attention to the most common defects and their sources. It does this by first looking at real-time process control mechanisms, understanding the various process variables and assessing their impact on the end product quality. This understanding drives the choice of sensing methods and the associated smart digital workflow to allow real-time control and mitigation of variation in the identified variables. Also, data from this workflow can be captured and used for the design of optimised dies and associated processes.

This is the subject of the second chapter that describes how the HDPC process can be simulated using Computational Fluid Dynamics based numerical modelling to understand the parameters affecting the process, analyse its performance, and to further select the optimum parameters that will lead to a better use of the material (magnesium in this case), and achieve less scrap rate, and higher efficiency rates.

Dr. Adel Aneiba
Prof. Cham Athwal
Prof. Hanifa Shah

Contents

Technical Papers

Industry 4.0: The Future of Manufacturing

Adel Aneiba, Hanifa Shah, Aftelak and Mak Sharma

School of Computing & Digital Technology, Birmingham City University,
Millennium Point, Birmingham, UK. B4 7XG.
Email :{ Adel.Aneiba, Hanifa.Shah, Andrew.Aftelak, Mak.Sharma}@bcu.ac.uk

Abstract

Digital transformation has become a priority appearing on many industrial organisations' agenda. Increasing productivity, staying competitive and reducing capital expenditure (Capex) as well as operation costs (Opex) is a key requirement for many market sectors especially in manufacturing. The digitisation of manufacturing will transform the way products and services are created and amongst other things change recruitment policies. The fourth industrial revolution (Industry 4.0 or "i4.0") has brought this transformation to many industrial sectors. The digital transition for many legacy factories to i4.0-enabled (Smart Factory) has been arduous. Smart Factory is the term used where machinery, products and systems are digitally connected along the manufacturing value chain. In this chapter, concepts surrounding i4.0 and its approaches to modernisation are defined as well as highlighting the strategic steps that need to be taken to achieve the i4.0 vision. Finally, the, latest technologies that enabled i4.0 solutions, will be addressed.

Keywords
Digital manufacturing, i4.0 Ecosystem, i4.0 Technologies, People 4.0.

INTRODUCTION

i4.0 can have different terms and definitions such as SMART Manufacturing, Smart Factory, Manufacturing 4.0 and Industrial Internet of Things, but they are all expressing one concept (Bassi, 2017). These terms are describing the ecosystem of the next era of manufacturing where all manufacturing value chain components (inbound logistics, operations, outbound logistics, marketing and sales) are working together to provide collective value to the industry (Nuseibah & Wolff, 2015). However, the definition for i4.0 was first announced in 2011 at the "Hannover Messe trade fair", as a result of an i4.0 working group formed by the German federal government (Sniderman et al, 2016). The Germany Trade and Investment group (GTAI) defines i4.0 as:

"A paradigm shift . . . made possible by technological advances which constitute a reversal of conventional production process logic. Simply put, this means that industrial production machinery no longer simply "processes" the product, but that the product communicates with the machinery to tell it exactly what to do".

I4.0 enables manufacturers and suppliers and to leverage new technological concepts like Augmented Reality, Digital Twin, Internet of Things, Cyber Physical Systems, Big Data and Cloud/Edge Computing. These promising technologies will help to create new products and services or to enhance existing ones. Such technological advances will reduce cost and increase productivity. The ideas, thoughts and technologies behind i4.0 are become more mature than before (Bassi, 2017). Most of these technologies have been adopted and implemented in many industrial sectors especially in the automotive industry, however, many software design and development aspects such as standardisation, specifications and modelling are still being developed. The fundamental principles of i4.0 can be described as: the use of the internet, production flexibility and virtualisation of process using data acquisition, data management and data decision making techniques.

The main motivation behind adopting the i4.0 initiative is to overcome the following hurdles: high cost and shortage of talented labour, short production cycle time, and small volume production (Cheng et al, 2016). Moving towards an information-based economy is a fundamental requirement by many governments around the world. i4.0 is at the centre of this new economic trend, therefore i4.0 can be seen as a catalyst for economic growth and support the knowledge economy of many leading nations such as USA, China, Japan, Germany and the UK. i4.0 is considered supportive for many national economies across the world (Gartner, 2016).

I4.0 ECOSYSTEM

i4.0 is a holistic industrial paradigm, whereby many business and technology elements are combining together to form an effective ecosystem. There is a need to have an ecosystem existing around the i4.0 phenomena which provides education, knowledge, facilities, funding and supportive legislation. i4.0 is a game changer, it's not just an updated version of a certain technology, it is a fully automated and connected manufacturing ecosystem (e.g. fully connected factory). The i4.0 ecosystem is a complex system of interdependent components that all work together to enable i4.0 services. In essence, an ecosystem is composed of interconnected living (active components) and non-living things (passive components) that all work together. In the i4.0 domain, the ecosystem consists of technical (hardware and software) and non-technical elements such as business partners, government regulatory bodies in manufacturing, customers, engineers' communities, industrial consultants, system integrators and policy makers. Figure 1 identifies the major areas that need to be considered for existing manufacturers or new entrants into the i4.0 domain. To establish a strong and competitive manufacturing strategy and to drive innovation, there is a need for smooth integration amongst all the ecosystem elements, between Information Communication Technology (ICT) and Operation Technology (OT).

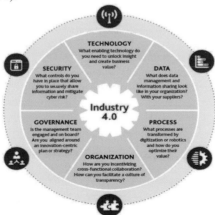

FIGURE 1: i4.0 Ecosystem (adapted from BDO, 2017)

Taking all the above elements into consideration when building an i4.0 business strategy, can lead organisations to build smarter manufacturing value chains and even powerful end-to-end ecosystems:

Data

Data is fundamental to the success of the i4.0 ecosystem, data and information gathered through the product life-cycle and corresponding services can assist manufacturers to understand their products and services much better, together with their customers' needs and their own business environment. Integration of multi data sources throughout the manufacturing value chain can strongly help business owners to provide a positive customer experience, as well as measuring their business performance. Sharing data among machines within factory settings and beyond is essential and has proved to be an effective strategy (Lee, 2013).

Smart Business Process

The distributed nature of i4.0 systems requires robust and smart business processes to be in place. This integration of real-time data provides an opportunity to optimise and automate manufacturing processes and improve performance. Modelling the complexity of the i4.0 business processes is not an easy task, but initiatives like "the Industry 4.0 Process Modeling Language (I4PML)" (Petrasch & Hentschke, 2016) are an important step towards modelling existing and new processes within the i4.0 ecosystem. Chapter 2 will address this topic in more detail.

Organisation

Creating an i4.0 culture across all levels of an organisation is key for achieving the transformation goals. The setting of shared goals, values and principles such as workplace fairness with clear transparent staffing policies will help organisations to accelerate the process of collaboration and build an innovative culture. Current organisational structures and cultures need to be ready to cope with rapid development in processes and technology for i4.0. Self-organisation and decentralised decision-making will become more important in the new era of i4.0. Related studies (BDO, 2017) have pointed out that "Management 4.0" will have to leave the traditional management norms and focus again even more closely on value creation.

Governance

The role of the senior management team in any organisation in achieving i4.0 business strategy is vital, they must be fully cognisant and fully engaged regarding the value of i4.0. This can be achieved by running targeted awareness programs specifically regarding the business value that i4.0 can bring to their businesses. Powerful leadership attributes are required to drive the organisation to achieve their goals for example, Brian Bacon, the chairman and founder of "Oxford Leadership" has defined i4.0 leadership as "The ability to rapidly align & engage empowered, networked teams with clarity of purpose and fierce resolve to win".

Security

i4.0 introduces new business models and technological systems which disrupt traditional ways of thinking and implementation solutions. This will have implications for required data inputs, connected processes as well as the communications and security protocols, thus potentially introducing new and yet unknown vulnerabilities. These vulnerabilities will compromise systems in many ways we had not imagined, hence putting i4.0 systems at a higher risk, therefore there will be a need for novel security approaches, methods and techniques to secure

4

these new systems and mitigate cyber risks. Chapter 7 addresses the security element of i4.0 in more detail.

Technology

To build a smarter and efficient manufacturing value chain, substantial research and development (R&D) is needed at an early stage to form a holistic i4.0 strategy. At the beginning of the manufacturing value chain, the R&D effort will accelerate the enhancement of the design cycle, reducing time to market, producing improved products and services (Acharyulu *et al*, 2015). Lateral thinking design engineers are the most valuable stakeholders at this stage. A better strategy can lead to a positive impact at the end of the value chain resulting in revenue increase and business growth. Table 1 shows key business objectives for manufacturers adopting i4.0.

TABLE 1: i4.0 Key Business Objectives, organised (Sniderman *et al*, 2016)

Business Operations	Productivity Improvements	• Maximising asset utilisation and minimizing downtime • Driving direct and indirect labour efficiency • Managing supply network costs and synchronization • Ensuring schedule and plan stability and accuracy
	Risk Reduction	• Ensuring raw material price and availability • Managing warranty and recalls effectively • Mitigating geographic risks
Business Growth	Incremental revenue	• Finding sources of growth for the core business • Growing aftermarket revenue streams • Deepening customer understanding and insights • Strengthening customer integration and channels
	New revenue	• Creating new products and service offerings • Expanding internationally and in emerging markets • Identifying attractive opportunities

I4.0 TECHNOLOGIES

Achieving business objectives while adopting i4.0 is largely dependent on the selected technologies alongside strong leadership and people skills. Certain emerging and developed technologies can offer tangible business opportunities to manufacturing leaders to improve their operations strategies and achieve their business objectives throughout the manufacturing value chain. Some of the key technologies that encapsulate the physical-to-digital-to-physical reach of i4.0 are recorded in table 2.

TABLE 2: i4.0 Technologies (Sniderman *et al*, 2016)

Product Impact	Potential IT/OT Applications
Physical → Digital	• Sensors and controls • Wearables • Augmented reality
Digital	• Signal aggregation • Optimization and prediction • Visualization and POU delivery • Cognitive and high-performance computing
Digital → Physical	• Additive manufacturing • Advanced materials • Autonomous robotics • Digital design and simulation

The technologies identified above, generally underpin and act as an enabler for i4.0. These technologies accelerate the automation task for machines and generate meaningful data to detect any possible failure or defects and predict any potential industrial trends (Lee, 2013). These will help in communicating, analysing and using information to carry additional intelligent actions back to the physical world to accomplish a physical-to-digital-to-physical transition. Below are the most dominant i4.0 technologies.

3D Printing (Additive Manufacturing)
Additive manufacturing systems play a major role for small volumes production at a minimum cost. In addition, it offers the ability to provide rapid design manufacturing solutions with shorter time-to-market. (Li & Lau, 2017). 3D printing is considered as a vital technology in i4.0 domain. It has offered a new way to model complex items and implement an otherwise time consuming design in a short time. 3D printing can be used for rapid prototyping to conceptualise future system or to add new feature to an existing one.

BlockChain
Decentralisation is a trend in many market sectors such as the automotive industry where distribution is a norm. Blockchain technology represents a logical choice to secure, manage and track the entire manufacturing value chain transactions. Many aspects of blockchain such as Smart contracts can make deployments more autonomous, intelligent and transparent. This will enable machines to carry out tasks faster by minimizing human intervention and accelerate the automation process (Hepp *et al*, 2018). The adoption rate of this technology varies and is dependent on the maturity of individual organisations. However, early adoption of blockchain technology may provide industrial companies with an edge over their competitors.

Big Data and Machine Learning
There is no doubt that i4.0 solutions will generate large volumes of data from different sources throughout the manufacturing value chain at various rates, structures and formats (i.e. Big Data). This requires advanced and innovative techniques to gather and pre-process the data. Then the data must be stored, managed, analysed and presented using sophisticated processing to turn it into meaningful insights, i.e. Information. Furthermore, from this information we can gain knowledge of the i4.0 system. With this knowledge we can start to predict the performance of the machines and production lines within an i4.0 context. This enablement will generate large volumes of data that require powerful analytics tools to manage and mine for business insights (i.e. wisdom) to help manufacturers assess their operations and boost their market position. Machine Learning algorithms are being widely adopted in the manufacturing arena to process and extract relevant features that are important to business to understand certain phenomena or solve certain problems (Wuest *et al*, 2016). Chapters 4, 5 and 6 address this subject in more detail.

Augmented Reality
Augmented and virtual reality have proved their worth in adding business value to many manufacturers. The concept of industrial augmented reality (IAR) has attracted various industrial stakeholders such as industrial engineers and manufacturing leaders. Several R&D attempts have been developed to use IAR systems to facilitate an early testing capability for prototype systems using virtual or mixed reality platforms (Fraga-Lamas *et al*, 2018). This is due to the latest advances in its interactive capabilities. AR concepts, techniques, tools and applications are explored in chapter 7

Smart Sensing/IoT

Sensing is one of the core i4.0 technologies. Sensors are installed mainly in individual manufacturing machines but can be installed across the entire manufacturing process, from raw material collection to the end-product. The role of installed sensors is essential to monitor the manufacturing process performance as well as the behaviour of the final product (Wright, 2014). Sensors are important for converting physical properties of machines into discrete and analogue signals. Various sensors are used in the manufacturing sector to trace vital data over the entire manufacturing process in real time and transmit it to the data centre on the edge or in the Cloud through an industrial communication network. These Big Data can be processed using platforms that employ applied machine learning and knowledge discovery techniques as well as tools to explore trends and insights.

DT (Digital Twin) and CPS (Cyber-Physical Systems)

The digital twin (DT) concept is becoming a hot topic in the i4.0 domain and is being used for global manufacturing digital transformation. It was named one of Gartner's Top 10 Strategic Technology Trends for 2017. The digital twin paves the way to cyber-physical integration making it a cost effective approach for manufacturers, designers and engineers. DT is all about simulating the physical objects/machines' behaviour via creating a virtual model using digital twin technology. DT is a powerful rapid development approach which promises significant value for many industrial organisations (Parrott & Warshaw, 2017). The developed virtual model understands the real-time status of a physical object by capturing data using advanced sensors to predict, estimate, and analyse dynamic behaviours and changes. Based on the simulation outputs from the digital twin peer, the physical entity/machine would respond to its environment accordingly. This will help manufacturing engineers to optimize the entire manufacturing process (Qi & Tao, 2018). Figure 2 illustrates these and related technologies that can be applied to the i4.0 domain.

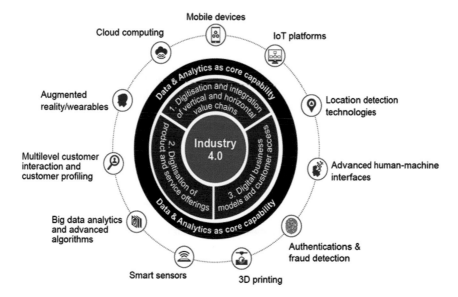

FIGURE 2: Major I4.0 Technologies (adapted from PWC, 2016)

TRANSITION CONSIDERATIONS TO I4.0

Prior to attaining an i4.0-enablement, industrial organisations that are adopting or planning to adopt i4.0 practices can expect numerous challenges relating to the integration of Information Technology (IT) and Operational Technology (OT). These challenges can be classified into two types, the first is at an organisational level where the internal operations and processes are required to improve to meet the i4.0 standards; whilst the second exists at the wider ecosystem level. These challenges are increased as connected technologies advance at a fast rate. For example, when companies are trying to integrate information technology and operational technology under the i4.0 practice at the organisational level, in this case most companies are struggling to find talent to design, implement and operate i4.0 systems.

Unskilled labour can lead to failure to adopt the new approach "i4.0", therefore, manufacturers need to adopt a proactive approach toward staff development when considering i4.0 applications. This can be done through developing an outsourcing strategy by partnering with outside organisations such as universities and apprenticeship programme providers to develop a steady stream of labour (Van Dinther *et al*, 2015).

Ecosystem challenges such as standardisation and interoperability are the most important components in the entire i4.0 ecosystem. As this element lies beyond companies' control, extra care needs to be taken when dealing with this matter. Normally, many of the systems behind i4.0 applications can impose integration challenges due to their proprietary nature. Ignoring the interoperability element can lead to a significant obstacle for full adoption of i4.0 technologies. To overcome this hurdle, industry leaders should work closely with partners to develop and unify industrial standards through peer consortiums, industry associations, and government industrial regulatory bodies as in (Din, 2018). These professional bodies can establish a set of standards to maximize the business value delivered by i4.0 investments (Amy *et al*, 2017).

Another important consideration within the i4.0 ecosystem is data ownership and control over the data that have been generated at various points of the manufacturing value chain. Regulating the data ownership across the value chain for many connected stakeholders is a real concern for many manufacturing organisations. Each stakeholder (supplier, customer, manufacturers…etc.) throughout the chain will be responsible for the data being generated in their working domain. The integration of these data sources can lead to product improvements and value creation for all stakeholders. Industrial leaders should think carefully about the benefits that this integration can bring to their business and consider data sharing, data ownership and data access agreements. The final important element of the ecosystem is the security of the generated data throughout the value chain. Security obviously is often mentioned as a concern in implementing i4.0 practices. Therefore, industrial leaders should not omit this element and start looking to evolve security solutions to protect their systems against a data breach and avoid any downtime events that might slow their operations. In general, the transformation roadmap will vary depending on the maturity of individual organisations.

To understand what manufacturers' leaders and business owners need to do to transform their business and enter the era of i4.0, six recommendations have been captured from successful i4.0-enabled companies (Petit *et al*, 2018). The below themes characterise core transformation elements such as harder capabilities (technology oriented) and softer enablers (human resources and vision). Table 3 summarises the required steps for digital transformation to i4.0.

TABLE 3: Essential guidelines for the digital transformation to i4.0 (Petit *et al*, 2018)

Theme	Recommended Actions
Vision, leadership and transformation plan	- Develop a clear and practical transformation digital vision and have a roadmap to execute it, progress and secure leadership support. - Communicating the vision across all levels of the organisation
Digital culture	- Building a robust digital culture across the organisation with clear core values such as openness, experimentation, flexibility, agility and collaboration.
Digital ecosystem	- Working closely with start-ups and partners across boundaries, both around products and services to drive business value.
Adopting i4.0 Technologies	- Invest in, and deploy, new and emerging digital technologies to develop smart, connected product and services.
People 4.0	- Recognise the importance of i4.0 digital skills across all levels of the organisation and setting a clear plan for recruiting talented people.
Data	- Taking full advantage of the collected data from different sources at various points in the manufacturing value chain.

DISCUSSION

A large challenge to implementing i4.0 is the heterogeneity of the systems involved. Different data exchange standards and formats exist such as OPC, OPC-UA and SEMI PV02. In addition, much manufacturing machinery is not interoperability-enabled. This will have an impact resulting in deficiencies in data management, minimizing the opportunities for full monitoring of the entire production process. Furthermore, omitting other related factors such as financial boundaries and holistic monitoring will reduce opportunities to gain business advantages (Cemernek *et al*, 2017). Furthermore, there are concerns regarding the influences of digitalisation on the economy and the labour market in many countries. Skilled labour is a major factor in the successful adoption of i4.0 and as such a comprehensive training plan and digital literacy activities for existing workforce and an efficient smart recruiting strategy for newcomers is paramount.

Despite the above challenges, many serious attempts have been made by leading automotive manufacturers towards i4.0 practice. Proactive Maintenance or Maintenance 4.0 is one practical example for i4.0 that has been proposed by (Dol & Bhinge, 2018). For instance, BMW, the automotive car company, has built a smart factory that has various smart workshops for major production processes such as stamping, body, coating and assembly. They employ smart robot systems to significantly improve efficiencies such as achieving water savings of 30%, energy savings of 40% and a 20% reduction in emissions. Another encouraging example is the automotive company Toyota. It has invested in UBER with $500 million to enhance self-driving projects by deploying more intelligence into their new designs and models, i4.0 technologies such as the digital twin (DT) and Cyber Physical Systems have been considered in this joint project (FT, 2018).

The above examples were chosen for their individual efforts, but there are well-known global initiatives launched by several countries. For example, Germany, the initiator of the i4.0 concept in Europe, has launched a national program in 2011 to drive forward i4.0 by developing common understanding across industry sectors. Following the progress made by Germany, Taiwan has launched their "Productivity 4.0" initiative that will be the centre of the digital transformation in the industry sector. (Chou *et al*, 2016). Moreover, in 2015, the Chinese government announced their "Made in China 2025" programme to promote the Chinese version of i4.0.

The aim of these initiatives is to enhance major manufacturing pillars such as productivity quality, delivery and flexibility based on technology convergence (Cemernek *et al* ,2017; Kang *et al*, 2016). i4.0 technologies can support various stakeholders from product designers to retailers who are involved in the product development cycle in achieving their tasks in a timely manner while maintaining quality. A full data analysis research has been carried out by various countries such as Germany to assess the impacts of i4.0 on productivity and revenue growth. They have found that productivity can be increased from 5% to 8% in the next ten years and reasonable saving can be obtained as much as 30% for general manufacturing costs such as overhead costs, operating costs and labour costs (Li & Lau, 2018). i4.0 can clearly bring benefits to many stakeholders, for example customers can use additive manufacturing technologies to build rapid prototyping in order to accelerate the design process (Sniderman *et al* 2017). Finally, technical concepts such as smart sensing, data aggregation, process optimisation, and decision making through prediction, enable manufacturers to get insights around their business performance and need (Schneider, 2015). This will help many organisations in better planning to provide better services and meet market demands.

CONCLUSIONS

i4.0 offers abundant opportunities for many industry sectors to enhance and control their business value chain. In addition, it allows manufacturers to gain a competitive edge by digitisation and integration of products and services. Integration can be among different machines, or different data sources and on a large scale among different industrial systems. The essence of system integration from the business point of view is providing industrial stakeholders with a unified view of the entire domain. i4.0 is enabling a new era of manufacturing intelligence and analytics. i4.0 produces new services and business models and can be described as a new growth engine for many industrial organisations. It is a bridge that takes manufacturers and business owners from the physical to the digital world where they obtain benefits and create business value.

Despite the challenges, business leaders should have a full unified view of the i4.0 ecosystem elements to unlock its potential. They must produce a detailed roadmap to achieve the i4.0 vision. This includes recruiting qualified people who can execute it and achieve business goals. Policy makers and business owners have to concentrate on all aspects and elements of the i4.0 ecosystem from the top with business strategic elements: vision and mission, industrial standards and cultural thinking down to adopting the latest digital industrial technologies and best practice in operations and management. For any i4.0 initiative to succeed, organisations need to understand how systems information, processes and external entities interact and interface with each other. Finally, industry leaders need to have a clear vision, mission and objectives for their i4.0 strategy to assess their market position, and identify direct requirements to achieve their business objectives, but the real challenge will remain in how this potential can be put into practice.

References

Acharyulu, S. G., Subbaiah, K. V., Rao, K. N. (2015) Value Chain Model For Steel Manufacturing Sector: A Case Study, International Journal of Managing Value and Supply Chains (IJMVSC) Vol. 6, No. 4, December 2015.

Amy J.C. Trappey, Charles V. Trappey, Usharani Hareesh Govindarajan, Allen C. Chuang, and John J. Sun. 2017. A review of essential standards and patent landscapes for the Internet of Things. Adv. Eng. Inform. 33, C (August 2017), 208-229.

Bassi, L. "I4.0: Hope, hype or revolution?," 2017 IEEE 3rd International Forum on Research and Technologies for Society and Industry (RTSI), Modena, 2017, pp. 1-6.

BDO. (2017) .Middle Market Manufacturer's Roadmap to I4.0, Special Report on I4.0, available from: https://www.bdo.com/insights/industries/manufacturing-distribution/the-middle-market-manufacturer-s-roadmap-to-in-(1)/the-middle-market-manufacturer-s-roadmap-to-indust, accessed on 16th August 2018.

Cemernek, D., Gursch, H. and Kern, R. (2017). "Big data as a promoter of i4.0: Lessons of the semiconductor industry," 2017 IEEE 15th International Conference on Industrial Informatics (INDIN), Emden, 2017, pp. 239-244.

Cheng, G., L. Liu, Qiang, X. and Liu, Y. (2016) "I4.0 Development and Application of Intelligent Manufacturing," International Conference on Information System and Artificial Intelligence (ISAI), Hong Kong, 2016, pp. 407-410.

Chou, C., Shen, C., Hsiao, H., Chen, C., Chang, H. and Chen, J. (2016). "Teachers' Pro-Industry Professional Cognitive to Adjust I4.0," 2016 International Symposium on Computer, Consumer and Control (IS3C), Xi'an, 2016, pp. 780-783

CPSC Strategic Plan 2016-2020 Executive Summary https://www.cpsc.gov/s3fs-public/CPSC_2016-2020_Strategic_Plan_Executive_Summary.pdf

Din, (2018). Indstry 4.0 Standardization , available from: https://www.din.de/en, published on 19.04.2018, accessed on 5th September, 2018.

Dol, S., and Bhinge, R. (2018) "SMART motor for i4.0," 2018 IEEMA Engineer Infinite Conference (eTechNxT), New Delhi, pp. 1-6.

Fraga-Lamas,P.,Fernández, T. M., Blanco-Novoa, O. and Vilar-Montesinos, M. A. 2018 . "A Review on Industrial Augmented Reality Systems for the I4.0 Shipyard," in IEEE Access, vol. 6, pp. 13358-13375, 2018.

FT, (2018). Toyota invests $500m in Uber driverless car partnership, available from: https://www.ft.com/content/1ca02574-aa2e-11e8-94bd-cba20d67390c, acccssed on 30th August 2018

Gartner's: 2016 Hype Cycle for Emerging Technologies.

Harnisch, (2015), Industry4.0: The Future of Productivity and Growth in Manufacturing Industries, The Boston Consulting Group.

Hepp, T., Wortner, P., Schönhals,A. and Gipp, B. 2018. Securing Physical Assets on the Blockchain: Linking a novel Object Identification Concept with Distributed Ledgers. In Proceedings of the 1st Workshop on Cryptocurrencies and Blockchains for Distributed Systems(CryBlock'18). ACM, New York, NY, USA, 60-65.

Hoske, Mark T. I4.0 and Internet of Things tools help streamline factory automation[J]. Control Engineering, 2015.

I40WG: Industrie 4.0 Working Group, "Recommendations for implementing the strategic initiative Industrie 4.0," 2013.

Kang, H.S., Lee, J.Y., Choi, S. et al. (2016). "Smart manufacturing: Past research, present findings, and future directions,", International Journal of Precision Engineering, and Manufacturing-Green Technology, vol. 3, no. 1, pp. 111–128,

Kuka. 2016. Hello Industrie 4.0: Smart Solutions For Smart Factories. Augsburg: KUKA Aktiengesellschaft

Lee J, Bagheri B, Kao HA. A cyber-physical systems architecture for I4.0-based manufacturing systems. Manufacturing Letters. 2015 Jan 31;3:18-23.

Lee, Jay, I4.0 in Big Data Environment, Harting Tech News 26, 2013. http://www.harting.com/fileadmin/harting/documents/lg/hartingtechnologygroup/news/tec-news/tecnews26/EN_tecNews26.pdf

Li, C. H. and Lau, H. K. (2017). "A critical review of product safety in i4.0 applications," 2017 IEEE International Conference on Industrial Engineering and Engineering Management (IEEM), Singapore, 2017, pp. 1661-1665.

Nuseibah, A. and Wolff, C. "Business ecosystem analysis framework," 2015 IEEE 8th International Conference on Intelligent Data Acquisition and Advanced Computing Systems: Technology and Applications (IDAACS), Warsaw, 2015, pp. 501-505

Parrott, A., and Warshaw, L. 2017 .I4.0 and the digital twin: Manufacturing meets its match, research article , Deloitte University Press , available from :

https://www2.deloitte.com/content/dam/Deloitte/cn/Documents/cip/deloitte-cn-cip-industry-4-0-digital-twin-technology-en-171215.pdf, accessed on 20th August

Petit, J.P., Buvat, J., Lange, U., Guiga, M., Brosset, P., Bacry, J. Nickerson, D. 2018. Digital Engineering: The new growth engine for discrete manufacturers, Capgemini Digital Transformation Institute, available from: https://www.capgemini.com/wp-content/uploads/2018/06/DTI_Digital-Engineering201806125_V08.pdf, accssed on 20th August.

Petrasch, R. and Hentschke, R. (2016). "Process modeling for industry 4.0 applications: Towards an industry 4.0 process modeling language and method," 2016 13th International Joint Conference on Computer Science and Software Engineering (JCSSE), Khon Kaen, 2016, pp. 1-5.

PWC, 2016. I4.0: Building the digital enterprise, Global I4.0 Survey, available from: https://www.pwc.com/gx/en/industries/industries-4.0/landing-page/industry-4.0-building-your-digital-enterprise-april-2016.pdf, accessed on Monday 20 august 2018

Qi, Q. and Tao, F. 2018. "Digital Twin and Big Data Towards Smart Manufacturing and I4.0: 360 Degree Comparison," in IEEE Access, vol. 6, pp. 3585-3593,.

Rüßmann, M., Lorenz, M., Gerbert, P., Waldner, M., Justus, J., Engel, P., & Harnisch, M. (2015). I4.0: The Future of Productivity and Growth in Manufacturing Industries. Boston Consulting Group.

Schneider Electric Software, (2015) ."Predictive asset analytics at power utilities," December 2015, http://software.schneider-electric.com/pdf/industry-solution/predictive-asset-analyticsat-power-utilities/, accessed August 25th , 2018.

Sniderman, B., Mahto, M., Cotteleer, M.J. (2016) I4.0 and manufacturing ecosystems: Exploring the world of connected enterprises, Deloitte University Press.

Van DintherM., Dochy, F., and Segers, M. (2015) "The contribution of assessment experiences to student teachers' self-efficacy in competence-based education," Teaching and Teacher Education, vol. 49, pp.45-55, 2015.

Wright, P. (2014). Cyber-physical product manufacturing, Manuf. Lett., 2(2), pp. 49–53.

Wuest,T., Weimer,D., Irgens, C. and Thoben , k. 2016. Machine learning in manufacturing: advantages, challenges, and applications, Production & Manufacturing Research, 4:1, 23-45.

Towards Smart Business Processes: Challenges, Practices, and Success Factors

Gerald Feldman Vahid Javidroozi and Hanifa Shah

School of Computing & Digital Technology, Birmingham City University,
Millennium Point, Birmingham, UK. B4 7XG.
Email: {gerald.feldman, vahid.javidroozi, hanifa.shah,}@bcu.ac.uk

Abstract

Industry 4.0 promotes growth, operational efficiencies, and new business models and services. However, to take full advantage of the Industry 4.0 landscape existing processes need to be transformed to facilitate automation, machine-to-machine communication and information flows. This chapter proposes a business process change model which outlines steps and activities that organisations should adopt as part of this transformation project. Also, it highlights the potential challenges that may be encountered during the business process change projects; the challenges are categorised, and success factor exemplars are offered as part of the smart process wheel.

Keywords

Smart Processes, Business Process Change (BPC), Smart Process Wheel

INTRODUCTION

Recent advancements in manufacturing technologies has led to a paradigm shift in the manufacturing sector, referred to as the fourth industrial revolution namely Industry 4.0. This shift influences customer expectations, increase data efficiency and promotes new business models. Industry 4.0 makes use of various technologies and techniques; this includes Cyber-Physical Systems (CPS), Internet of Things (IoT), cloud computing, blockchain, Enterprise Resources Planning (ERP) systems and other technologies (Moeuf et al., 2017). While there are numerous definitions for Industry 4.0, Hoffmann et al. (2017) suggest that Industry 4.0 can be considered as a digital interconnection of products and services to enable automation and self-optimisation with minimal human interventions. Lu (2017) advocates that Industry 4.0 allows IT-enabled customisation of manufactured products leading to automation and flexible adaptation of the production chain leading to operational efficiency, productivity and automation. For example, one of the core roles of CPS is to support agile production by integrating various data and knowledge, which can result in improved effectiveness and efficiency (Lu, 2017). The implementation of Industry 4.0 results in horizontal, vertical and end-to-end integration of the different technologies, resources, products and systems, which improves management of complex business processes. The integration of these different technologies, systems and resources facilitates autonomous sharing of information, control of processes and optimised decision-making, which are the core foundation of a smart factory.

Smart factories offer manufacturing firms an opportunity to leverage Industry 4.0 technologies to integrate and extend processes, become intelligent, dynamic and flexible to market demands. Also, the integration of real-time data provides an opportunity to optimise and automate manufacturing processes and improve performance. Hoffman et al. (2017) implied that smart factories are dependent on processes that can be fully automated, thus enabling machine-to-machine communication and material transfer with minimum human intercession. As part of their study, they explored the potential implication of Industry 4.0 and highlighted the following Just-in-Time (JIT) / Just-in-Sequence (JIS) processes characteristics (Figure 1).

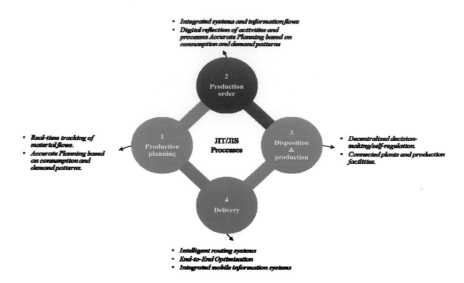

FIGURE 1: Industry 4.0 Characteristics for JIT/JIS processes (adapted from Hoffman *et al.,* 2017)

Drawing from Figure 1, Industry 4.0 facilitates real-time tracking of materials flow, generally achieved when there is direct machine-to-machine communication through the use of sensors to support sharing of data and automation of material transfer between machines with minimal human intervention. Also, integration of systems enhances information flows, decision-making, and process transparency resulting in an intelligent end-to-end optimisation of tasks and most importantly facilitate the transformation of business models. This transformation leads to wide-ranging changes in all areas of value creation, such as (i) availability of goods and services with the prospect of autonomous delivering with the aim of responding faster and being more adaptable to volatile market demand; (ii) improvements in transparency and traceability offered by connected smart processes and components which facilitate autonomous awareness of components and monitoring of process parameters which also increase efficiency and productivity. Smart processes promote autonomous operations, self-regulation and transparent activities assisted by machine-machine communication and sharing of data. However, Moeuf *et al.* (2017) indicate that many manufacturing firms have implemented traditional business processes and the introduction of Industry 4.0 would potentially disrupt these processes. Therefore, there is a need for these processes to be transformed to accommodate the technological solutions offered as part of the Industry 4.0 landscape and support seamless integration of technology, processes, data and people, along with coordination of services and physical flows.

ENTERPRISE SYSTEMS INTEGRATION (ESI)

According to Xu (2018), Enterprise Systems Integration (ESI) plays a significant role in integrating business processes and facilitating sharing of information across all business units. ESI introduces changes and improvements to operations and elements of the business strategy, which are created by business processes. Business processes are systematic rules, which connect the input to the output of an organisation, thus, implement the business objectives. Other components including people, management, roles, tasks, information flow, and technology add value to the inputs and generate some outputs, such as products and services to the customers. Therefore, business processes affect the enterprises' capabilities for production or service delivery, supporting the notion that business processes are the primary drivers that help to perform the tasks through a seamless process flow across related departments (Harmon, 2014). Javidroozi *et al.* (2015) concluded that during ESI, the most significant change is undertaken on business processes, suggesting that technology is an enabler which is used to realise and manage this transition. Morton and Hu (2008) suggest that for a successful ESI, the organisational structure should fit the systems integrator and technology (such as ERP, CPS). As a result, the enhancement of business processes' performance through undertaking an appropriate change approach, to provide intercommunication, interoperation, and consequently integration amongst organisational components, is a necessity to support the leveraging of industry 4.0 technologies. According to Lodhi *et al.* (2013) and Jurisch *et al.* (2014), there is a direct relationship between a successful BPC and the whole enterprise's performance. Thus, the next sections discuss BPC practices, approaches, stages, challenges, and success factors, as the foundation that would allow the creation of smart processes.

Business Process Change (BPC)
For an effective systems integration, BPC needs to be managed and planned carefully (Jurisch et al., 2014). Accordingly, the following actions should be undertaken: (i) an appropriate BPC approach should be taken (Jurisch et al., 2014); (ii) some stages along with their activities should be followed (Harmon, 2007); and (iii) the challenges encountered during the BPC procedure should be addressed (Harmon, 2007; Jurisch et al., 2014). While the terms Business Process Management (BPM), Business Process Reengineering (BPR), and BPC have been utilised interchangeably, BPC is an enhancement procedure, which develops business processes in two different approaches/modes: revolutionary/radical or evolutionary Javidroozi *et al.* (2015). This implies that BPM is an approach/type/technique for conducting BPC, which encompasses other techniques and tools such as Business Process Transformation (BPT), Total Quality Management (TQM), and Six Sigma. Nevertheless, BPM is a comprehensive and systematic approach, which includes all other tools, techniques, and approaches for addressing BPC challenges. Each approach comprises different tools and techniques such as BPR, BPI, TQM, and so on. Figure 2 illustrates further the approaches and some of the BPC tools and techniques. Even-though Industry 4.0 introduces radical changes that revolutionise the manufacturing industry it is essential to take into account both BPC approaches when conducting BPC as part of developing smart processes.

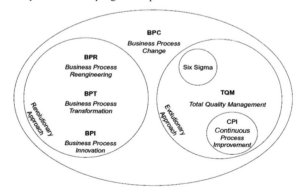

FIGURE 2: BPC approaches and types (adapted from Jurisch et al., 2014)

BPC stages

Earlier researchers such as Harmon and Trends (2010), and Kettinger et al. (1997) have suggested various methodologies for BPC. However, despite the different characterisation and different terminologies, all methodologies emphasise similar aspects and adhere to the same rules. Javidroozi et al. (2016) have critically reviewed these methodologies and proposed a BPC model .Figure 3 offers steps to assist digital transformation that can drive the development of smart business processes.

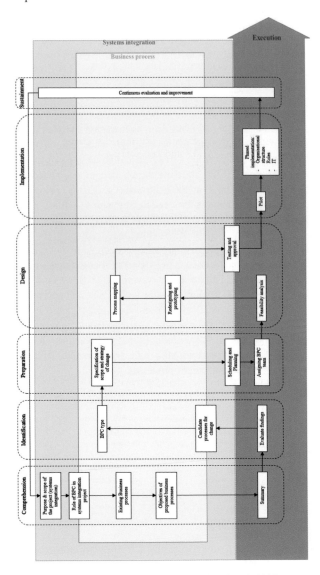

FIGURE 3: BPC model (Source: Javidroozi et al., 2016)

The BPC model focuses on system integration as the primary project goal (Table 3 provides a summary of the steps). The steps proposed can be utilised for transforming existing processes in a manufacturing firm to make them more compatible to support the drive towards smart factories. However, the stages are carried out at various levels, including systems integration, business process, and execution level. In other words, the activities of the business process level are not separated from the systems integration level, because changing business processes are designed within systems integration. Hence, the activities of every BPC step are performed on these three levels.

TABLE 1: Description of the BPC model stages

Stage	Description
Comprehension	The following activities: understanding, analysis, and evaluation will be undertaken with the aim of identifying the goal and purpose of BPC. For example, if the primary goal is system integration as part of the smart factory development, therefore at this stage it would be essential to understand what the systems integration project objectives are, which can lead to aligning business processes for this purpose. Thus, analysis and in depth understanding of all current business processes are necessary. This will also develop the objectives of new business processes.
Identification	In this stage, the summary of all business process analysis findings from the previous step is evaluated to determine if these processes meet the integration requirements. Also, the business processes, which are fully aligned with the objectives of the main project will be recognised and documented. After that, the approach and type of BPC will be identified. At this stage, the radicalness of the change will be determined, and appropriate mode of change will be assigned to identify the approach to use (details on how to assess the level of radicalness is available in (Javidroozi et al., 2016).
Preparation	After the identification of the candidate business processes for change and the BPC type, the scope and strategy of the change should be specified, and all scheduling and planning activities will be carried out. Also, all other key business drivers including the organisation, human resources, and possible technological resources need to be identified and prepared for the change. Additionally, the appropriate change team including business process experts, who are fully informed about the candidate processes will be assigned. Moreover, top management support would be requested and all stakeholders and other employees will be informed about the change.
Design	The actual changing and redesigning activities including brainstorming, defining and analysing new process concept, prototyping, designing, and documenting new processes according to identified change approach are carried out in this step by a team, responsible for the change. Appropriate techniques for process mapping and prototyping will be applied, along with evaluating the benefits for the business, costs and feasibility to select the best option.
Implementation	Having the prototype tested and approved (referred to as a phased approach) is a more preferred implementation approach for most of the BPCs, especially for those which are highly visible internally and externally, and involved with revenues, customers, or valuable employees. A phased approach is also an economical method of implementation, which generates some financial benefit from BPC in an earlier time. In this stage changes to organisation structure, roles, and IT will be carried out. BPC techniques such as TQM and Six Sigma will also be applied for fulfilling this step.
Sustainment	The last step of changing business processes is to evaluate and improve the new processes' performance continuously and assess if they have addressed the requirements. This allows the organisation to monitor and control the business processes after the change continuously.

BPC challenges, practices, and success factors

Any changes introduced, be it technology or process, would present significant challenges and risks to the organisation. Similarly, BPC involves numerous types of challenges that can arise in any of its steps. Various tools, techniques, approaches, and success factors are proposed to facilitate the addressing of these BPC challenges. Therefore, one of the main steps towards smart process is the identification of the BPC challenges and their success factors. This chapter proposes a conceptual 'smart process wheel' (Figure 4), which categorises the different challenges that a manufacturing firm may encounter when developing smart processes. The challenges have been categorised into five dimensions based on Kettinger and Grover's (1995) BPC model, as well as Javidroozi *et al.'s* (2015) systems integration model.

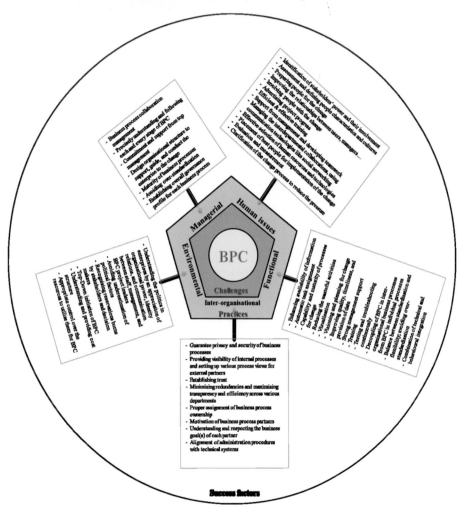

FIGURE 4: Conceptual Smart Process Wheel

The five BPC challenges dimensions are:

1.   Managerial: this includes challenges such as clarification and understanding of business processes, BPC monitoring, risk assessment, governance.

2.   Functional: these are mostly related to operational aspects of the organisation; the challenges include efficiency, quality assurance, and complexity.

3.   Inter-organisational: these are more concerned with ensuring collaboration, communication, and integration among systems; challenges include interoperability, data sharing, and inter-dependencies.

4.   Human issues: it is well established that people play an essential role during BPC; the challenges associated with human issues include people's acceptance, commitment, culture, knowledge of the users, stakeholders.
5.   Environmental: these challenges are related to the external and internal influences that can impact the transformation; the challenges could include costs, politics and other external factors.

The processing wheel offers success factors as exemplars, and when these are used along with BPM tools and techniques, it will promote the development of best practices for BPC. Next, the best practices would be utilised in various contexts, so that the smart processes will be established. Hence, the smart process wheel would be useful for any firm that attempts to implement ESI to change its processes, whether this is part of an Industry 4.0 implementation or any other digital transformation project.

CONCLUSIONS

Industry 4.0 technologies can significantly improve operations and introduce new business models that can help manufacturing firms find new opportunities for value creation. However, to fully leverage these capabilities, there is a need to integrate technology, processes, people and data. The integration of these elements is not straightforward as these changes usually introduce risks and challenges, especially since business processes are the core elements that need to be transformed as part of any system integration. Therefore, it is essential to follow precise steps and activities to support any digital transformation projects. As a result, this chapter proposed a BPC model, that suggests stages and activities that can be used to identify smart practices that can be used to design smart business processes.

Additionally, understanding the practices, challenges and success factors during any BPC project is critical to the success of the project. Hence, a conceptual smart wheel is presented, which categorises BPC challenges and provides critical success factors exemplars that can be used in conjunction with BPM tools to address the challenges that arise during BPC projects.

It should be noted that these challenges and success factors are not exhaustive. One reason for this is that each firm may approach BPC differently. Hence a detailed study needs to be undertaken to capture all the challenges so that relevant success factors could be offered that best fit the firm undertaking the business transformation.

References

Harmon, P., 2007. Business process change : a guide for business managers and BPM and six sigma professionals. Elsevier.

Harmon, P., 2014. Business Process Change: A business process management guide for managers and process professionals. Elsevier Science.

Hofmann, E. and Rüsch, M., 2017. Industry 4.0 and the current status as well as future prospects on logistics. Computers in Industry, 89, pp.23-34.

Javidroozi, V., Shah, H., Amini, A. and Feldman, G., 2016. Business process change: A guide for implementers. In: Proceedings of the International Conference on e-Learning, e-Business, Enterprise Information Systems, and e-Government (EEE), pp. 93–99.

Javidroozi, V., Shah, H., Cole, A. and Amini, A., 2015. Towards a City's Systems Integration Model for Smart City Development: A Conceptualization. In 2015 International Conference on Computational Science and Computational Intelligence (CSCI), 312–317.

Jurisch, M.C., Palka, W., Wolf, P. and Krcmar, H., 2014. Which capabilities matter for successful business process change? Business Process Management Journal, Emerald Group Publishing Limited, 20(1), 47–67.

Kettinger, W.J. and Grover, V., 1995. Toward a theory of business process change management - ProQuest. Journal of Management Information Systems, 12(1), 9.

Kettinger, W.J., Teng, J.T.C. and Guha, S., 1997. Business process change: A study of methodologies, techniques, and tools - ProQuest. MIS Quarterly, 21(1), 55–80.

Lodhi, A., Köppen V. and Saake, G., 2013. Business Process Improvement Framework and Representational Support. In: Kudělka M, Pokorný J, Snášel V, et al. (eds), Proceedings of the Third International Conference on Intelligent Human Computer Interaction, Advances in Intelligent Systems and Computing, Berlin, Heidelberg, Springer Berlin Heidelberg, pp. 155–167.

Lu, Y., 2017. Industry 4.0: A survey on technologies, applications and open research issues. Journal of Industrial Information Integration, 6, pp.1-10.

Moeuf, A., Pellerin, R., Lamouri, S., Tamayo-Giraldo, S. and Barbaray, R., 2018. The industrial management of SMEs in the era of Industry 4.0. International Journal of Production Research, 56(3), pp.1118-1136.

Morton, N.A. and Hu, Q., 2008. Implications of the fit between organizational structure and ERP: A structural contingency theory perspective. International Journal of Information Management, 28(5), 391–402.

Valiris, G. and Glykas, M., 1999. Critical review of existing BPR methodologies: The need for a holistic approach. Business Process Management Journal, MCB UP Ltd, 5(1), 65–86.

Xu, L.D., Xu, E.L. and Li, L., 2018. Industry 4.0: state of the art and future trends. International Journal of Production Research, 56(8), pp.2941-2962.

Smart Sensors and Sensor Intelligence in the Digitalized Manufacture Process

Wenyan Wu

School of Engineering and the Built Environment Birmingham City University,
4 Cardigan Street, Birmingham, UK. B4 7BD
Email: Wenyan.wu@bcu.ac.uk

Abstract
The purpose of this paper is to provide an outline of how smart sensor technology and sensor intelligence can be applied to the manufacturing process in industry 4.0. This chapter provides an overview of key smart sensor technologies and sensor intelligence in industrial processes that act as intelligent agents to sense and further process the collected data and transmit it. In this manner dynamic configuring of sensors is enabled to provide targeted and specific data for particular purposes to achieve an optimised and efficient industrial process.

Keywords
Smart Sensor, Sensor Intelligence, Industry 4.0, Digital Manufacture

INTRODUCTION

Modern industrial development has led to the new era of Industry 4.0. as initially proposed for developing German economy (Vogel & Hess 2011). The automation of production based on electronics and internet technology has been developed for several decades; whilst the recently developed Industry 4.0 focuses on cyber physical systems (CPS) production, based on heterogeneous data and knowledge integration to achieve a higher level of operational efficiency and productivity, as well as a higher level of automatization (Lee et al 2015). The main roles of CPS are to fulfill the agile and dynamic requirements of production, and to improve the effectiveness and efficiency of the entire industry. Industry 4.0 involves numerous technologies and associated paradigms, including Radio Frequency Identification (RFID), Enterprise Resource Planning (ERP), Internet of Things (IoT), cloud-based manufacturing, and social product development (Thames and Schaefer 2016, Georgakopoulos, 2016, Kube &Rinn 2014, Lin et al 2016 , Pfeiffer 2016, Roblek, et al, 2016,Wan et al 2106).

Industry 4.0 can be summarized as an integrated, adapted, optimized, service-oriented, and interoperable manufacturing process which is correlated with algorithms, big data, and high technologies. The major features of Industry 4.0 are digitization, optimization, and customization of production; automation and adaptation; human machine interaction (HMI); value-added services and businesses, and automatic data exchange and communication. These features not only are highly correlated with internet technologies and advanced algorithms, but they also indicate that Industry 4.0 is an industrial process of value adding and knowledge management.

Industry 4.0 facilitates interconnection and computerization into the traditional industry. It provides IT-enabled mass customization of manufactured products; to make automatic and flexible adaptation of the production chain; to facilitate communication among parts, products, and machines; to apply human-machine interaction (HMI) paradigms; to achieve IoT-enabled production optimization in smart factories; and to provide new types of services and business models of interaction in the value chain (Shafiq et al. 2015, 2016). Industry 4.0 brings disruptive changes to supply chains, business models, and business processes (Schmidt 2015).

Cyber-Physical Systems (CPS) are expected to offer promising solutions to transform the operation and role of many existing industrial systems (Bondar et al 2017, Mao et al 2016, Yan et al 2015). CPS is seen as the convergence of the physical and digital worlds: data and information are exchanged among embedded devices, wireless applications, or even clouds. A complex, dynamic and integrated CPS will support collaboration of planning, analysis, modeling, design, implemention and maintenance in the manufacturing process. CPS combine information and materials, where decentralization and autonomy play important roles in improving the overall industrial performance (Harrison & Ammad 2016, Bagheri *et al* 2015). CPS can also consist of micro-controllers that control the physical sensors and actuators. With the advances in wireless communication, smartphones, and sensor network technologies, CPS will make a large impact on new ICT and enterprise systems technologies.

The CPS of Industry 4.0 will be activated and enforced by the development of computational entities, data-related procedures, manufacturing automation and technology, and information and communication technologies (ICT). The manufacturing systems by integrating with CPS will be a new generation of industry, which involves humans, machines, and product, and combines computation, networking, and physical processes together in the production process in order to make a more cost- and time-efficient production process (Albers *et al* 2016)

Networked production and process control in industrial process environments determine the industrial future and Industry 4.0 is made possible by using Smart Sensors to support dynamic, real-time optimized, and self-adaptive industry processes. Practical operational statuses from machine will be digitized and collected from smart sensor and become data, that is shared automatically with the process controller. As providers of data, sensor technology is the prerequisite for successful implementation of Industry 4.0.

The added value of sensor communication depends significantly on the quality and stability of the delivered data. Smart Sensors technology enhances sensing to ensure stability during detection and recording of measured values. Sensors, machines, and humans involved can communicate with each other at any time in industry 4.0. This information at the factory gateways or edge and cloud also allow operation and data management from and to the outside and further application. This cooperation between sensor technology and humans makes the industrial process more transparent, productive, and profitable.

Sustainable industrial operations encompasses both material management as well as operational checks and machine and production monitoring. This makes it possible to reduce stock levels and shorten throughput times. Sensor solutions for process monitoring and quality assurance provide added flexibility and autonomous adaptation in the case of changes to quality and products. As a result, they offer resource efficiency, a lower reject rate, and a high level of throughput.

One of the major challenges associated with Industry 4.0 is making production processes flexible. Many production companies are looking to Industry 4.0 to provide ways of setting up flexible production processes with a high degree of automation. State-of-the-art manufacture already contains elements of the requirements of Industry 4.0 – and are waiting for their full potential to be exploited. The factory of the future is increasingly set to blur the lines between humans and machines, with teams containing robots and people working side by side. This requires a different approach to safety that addresses the need to respond to a range of situations with high flexibility aided by sensor technology and sensor intelligence.

This chapter will review how smart sensor technologies and sensor intelligence in industrial processes act as an intelligent agent to sense and further process the collected data and transmit it, to provide the specific data for particular purposes for an optimised and efficient industrial process in Industry 4.0, with an example in high pressure die casting.

SMART SENSOR TECHNOLOGY

Intelligent measurement technology is required at every step of the process, and these measurements are carried out using a wide array of methods (See Figure 1). Various sensor technologies developed currently have been adopted and integrated into the production process, such as optical sensor and ultrasound sensor technology. Industrial wireless sensor networks connect sensors and devices and collect and transmit data in the manufacturing process in the context of industry 4.0 (Li *et al* 2015)

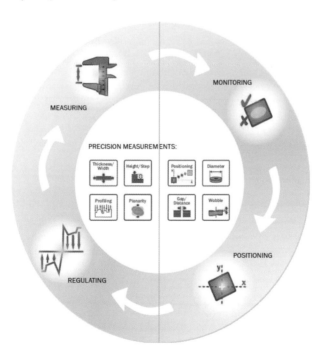

FIGURE 1: Intelligent measurement technology (SICKInsight)

Optical sensor technology

A non-contact, precise, and speedy technology: the benefits of optical measuring sensors in contrast to mechanical measuring tools are obvious. There is no need to touch the object to be measured so that sensitive materials are protected from distortion or damage. Optical measuring sensors can also be beneficial if the object's surface is difficult to access. Whether you opt for 1D or 2D, or 2D and 3D vision solutions: the high precision measurement laser allows triangulation and chromatic confocal measurement of the object directly in the production process helping to guarantee added efficiency, while making sure of quality (Everton *et al* 2016).

There are the various applications using intelligent optical sensor measurement technology. Displacement measurement sensors especially show their strength when it comes to dealing with fragile components to achieve precision detection, spotting even the tiniest material faults and micro-cracks. The sensor array in the sensor unit can deliver measurement results with the maximum possible precision, without need to worry about complicated calibration. With displacement measurement sensors, grippers are precisely positioned using non-contact technology for Automotive and parts suppliers for precision on the production line. For 2D or 3D vision and displacement measurement sensors, the combination of various types of technology brings its own benefits: for instance, displacement measurement sensors make sure that electronics cards are in the right position. 2D vision sensors measure holes' diameters with a high level of accuracy before 3D vision sensors then determine the height and volume of the electronics cards, making it easier to locate shape defects (Barua *et al* 2014).

A broad spectrum of vision sensors offer a great opportunity for industrial manufacturers starting with compact devices that are easy to integrate, through configurable stand-alone solutions, and beyond to programmable high-speed cameras for the most demanding of requirements. The programmable sensor system delivers a high level of development flexibility to minimize complexity, costs, and risks in the implementation of customized image processing solutions. It is used to create new solutions from both established modules and integrable functions from various image processing libraries, such as OpenCV, which provide the perfect match for customers' requirements and are compatible with tasks in the context of Industry 4.0, such tasks include quality control, track and trace, object data capture, and predictive maintenance.

There are a wide range of configurable and programmable vision sensors in addition to the normal 2D camera. A 3D sensor can maximise performance with additional height monitoring. This type of camera allows us to generate very high-quality 3D data at a very high speed. For example the inspection of magnesium bricks with 3D vision technology from (Leo 2017) allows quality control without downtime. Producers of building materials like to ensure that their products achieve the highest quality possible, and in the production of special bricks for blast furnaces, which are particularly susceptible to surface damage, carrying out quality control during the production process is indispensable. A system has been developed where bricks are scanned during transport on conveyor belts with the 3D vision sensors to create 3D models of each individual brick. The 3D models can be used to determine the precise dimensions of the brick and the extent of its damage. The 3D vision sensors operate based on the principle of triangulation distance measurement. The line laser beam is integrated into the sensor housing, projects a light track on objects, allowing their profile to be determined. The 3D sensors are able to use these profiles to create precise 3D images of the magnesium bricks, measuring them with high precision and detecting volume errors. This allows the quality of the bricks to be checked during the production process.

These programable 3D vision sensors can connect to a network and communicate with each other; communication betwen sensors allows operation to continue without being connected to a computer. One of the 3D vision sensors can be designated as the control sensor, collecting information from subordinate sensors and transmitting the measurement results to the foundry robot, which is responsible for the mechanical loading and unloading of bricks from the conveyor belts. At the same time, the 3D vision sensors communicate with the control panel. This control panel allows for the entry of the measurement parameters and, where necessary, data archiving for subsequent inspection.

Ultrasonic sensor technology
Cutting-edge ultrasonic sensor technology, with more efficient electronics, has demonstrated good benefits to users. Background noise is a real poison for accurate ultrasonic measurements. For example, expansions in pipelines, valves, plant vibrations, or pressure regulators often cause critical levels of noise for the ultrasonic measurement process. Tiny amounts of noise can have a huge impact on ultrasonic sensors. These noises can affect the way signals are received, particularly in the high frequency range between 85 and 200 kHz. This in turn can affect the signal quality, leading to uncertain measurements. Current new ultrasonic sensors and optimized electronics has managed to improve the system's resistance to disruptive noises in the application such that noise no longer has such a negative impact on measurements. Built-in pressure and temperature sensors allow the automated calculation of minimal geometric changes to the meter in a bid to improve the accuracy of the measurement result (Shin *et al* 2016).

Ultrasonic and time-of-flight measurement offers complete flow measurement which is flexible for all industries and fluids. The non-contact flow sensor detects the flow volume of conductive and non-conductive fluids based on ultrasonic technology. The ultrasonic flowmeter is suitable for measuring tasks in hygienic conditions. The compact and rugged design offers a wide variety of application possibilities, including those where space restrictions or aggressive media play a role. For example, the new fluid sensors offer calibration-free measurements no matter which medium they are used in, ensuring a high level of flexibility. Plants do not have to be converted or operated in parallel when the fluid or medium is being changed. The digital communication protocol also allows the process data to be integrated into an automation network.

Small quantities and individualized mass products are the key words of Industry 4.0. A machine must be able to handle variable product infeed and adapt to different formats. Sensors and actuators make such an adaptation possible. Any product size and shape can be produced flexibly on one machine. Current broad portfolio of sensor products and solutions of sensor technology allows us to offer many different possibilities and methods for creating the foundation for more flexible processes. This involves the concepts of digitization, intelligence, and networking, which will enable production and logistics systems to optimize and control themselves autonomously. Intelligent sensor technology enables this flexibility. This technology makes it possible to collect production data in real time and to optimize machines, being able to adapt to significantly changing conditions. Fast, software-supported format changes can reduce downtime and optimize material utilization and packaging processes. For example, in packaging machines it is primarily contrast sensors that are used for recognizing marks. The contrast sensors can detect the smallest contrasts at the highest speeds. They detect minute grayscale variations between the mark and the background on matte, shiny, or transparent surfaces. The contrast sensor has to be taught for optimal recognition of the marks and with multiple sensors built into a machine, this will take a lot of time. However, if the sensor has been added intelligence within a sensor unit, once parameters have been taught to the contrast sensor they will be stored in the controller. If the format changes, the corresponding information is simply recalled. This will save time and cost.

Current smart sensors offer additional advantages, along with conventional sensor detection, the current smart sensor will be able to provide additional information via I/O connection. The connection enables constant data diagnostic and learning functions, which is indicative of process reliability. If any changes of the process is in progress, the quality of function reports back immediately through sensor I/O connection. These additional integrated functions with smart sensor allow you to produce new and higher-quality information beyond detection together with the customer's desired application.

SENSOR INTELLIGENCE

Communication-enabled sensors combining smart sensor intelligence with additional integrated functions offer a great deal of potential. Industial communication and sensor integration is now gaining increasing acceptance in an ever greater number of applications – the manufacturer-independent communication technology is also a catalyst for innovative sensor solutions and supports the global availability of data and information required by Industry 4.0. The smart sensors ultilise their communication ability to reliably acquire data, as well as to communicate and run diagnostics with intelligent algorithms. The integrated sensor combined with additional functions offers huge potential in terms of machine productivity and reliablity, expecially for remote automation tasks in industrial processes. Sensor intelligence is seen as a foundation of Industry 4.0 (SICKinsight)

Self-diagnostics via intelligent algorithms makes predictive maintenance possible. The components of machines and plant in the production environment are constantly subjected to environmental influences such as temperature, material, humidity and vibrations. Current smart sensors are designed to operate in harsh application conditions in terms of their mechanical, electrical and optical properties, and have improved their performance when subject to heavy loads and high throughput by virtue of their self-monitoring and self adaptive functions. Diagnostic data and intelligent algorithms can be used at machine-level (but also in cloud-based) analysis tools in order to anticipate potential faults in good time and to prevent them from occurring by means of predictive maintenance. Smart sensors' settings can be visualised and reconfigured for the benefit of the machine operator.

The potential of smart sensors is increasing and leading towards step-wise increases in efficiency for many tasks in industrial processes, such as downloading parameters for fast changeover, easy device replacement, formula management and condition monitoring. Newly developed sensor technology have additional integrated functions, allowing computing power to move from the automation system to field devices – offering a sustainable approach for building more efficient and better-performing automation networks. The integrated additional functions also allow you to generate new, higher-quality information that goes over and beyond object detection, depending on the desired application. This information can be generated from the integrated sensing system and then provided for the higher-level systems as necessary (PLC, ERP, the cloud).

Flexibility and productivity are major trends in the field of industrial automation and this requires flexible safety concepts to be developed and deployed in production processes. The wide range of safety-related sensors and controller solutions in the market allow you to customise the requirement and design protection mechanisms in a flexible manner and adapt them to real situations. The controller, using a flexible safety algorithm, offers a wide variety of options for programming for monitoring scenarios and integrating various safety sensors. This sensor intelligence can process the signals from other sensors to enhance the automation solution as a whole.

Sensor Intelligence has also integrated with robots, which are already able to operate without being surrounded by a safety fence. Safety laser scanners monitor the defined robot surroundings and are connected to the safety controller of the robot. The easy-to-program protective field geometries can be easily adapted to the individual layout. Modern robot systems feature safely monitored axles and drives. Safety limits can be set for the robot operation space in the robot's controller. The protective field is always larger than the working area of the robot. Stopping/run-down times and approach speeds must also be taken into account. This ensures that any personnel are detected in good time and that the robot is stopped before a hazard arises for the person. These new communication options and the functionalities of safe sensors, combined with non-safe sensors, represent beneficial application solutions for reliability and productivity.

New safety sensor technologies currently in development will enable even closer coordination with manufacturing processes in the future. For example, intelligent algorithms in sensor systems are making it possible to favour a continuous machine response based on the current position. The machine no longer triggers a complete shutdown, but instead results in the working speed being reduced to an appropriate level or the directions of movement being modified so that the person's safety is ensured at all times and yet production can still continue.

Recently an open platform for programmable sensors has been developed. These sensor systems offer system integrators and manufacturers means to develop application solutions to fit specific requirements' descriptions; from precisely designing the perfect online user interface, through selecting the most suitable programming technique to distributing the software on various hardware platforms.

INTELLIGENT SENSOR APPLICATION IN DIGITAL MANUFACTURE

Sensors will improve the quality and consistency of the manufacturing process. For example, die casters manufacture a large and diverse array of products. Using machines to rapidly inject molten alloys or magnesium into metal moulds, die casters produce near-net-shape parts at high production rates. Typical part cycle times range from 30 to 120 seconds, and metal injection is completed in times as low as 50 milliseconds. Improper filling of the die cavity can result in entrapped gases and a poor quality casting. Proper performance in die casting depends on a combination of effective die design; robust mechanical operation and control of the die casting machine; the delivery of molten metal at the right temperature and cleanliness; controlled thermal management of the die; and metal pressure intensification at the end of the injection cycle to feed shrinkage. Typically, die casters monitor machine variables at only discrete points. Advanced sensor technologies are available to directly measure critical process parameters. If critical variables are continuously monitored and controlled, problems can be detected and solved during the casting cycle. This will lead to less scrap, improved surface finish, higher dimensional repeatability, and improved internal integrity. Current research has developed the use of vibration sensors (accelerometers) for machine diagnostics, allowing problems to be detected and solved during the casting cycle. Vibration diagnostics often provide insight into both normal and anomalous operational characteristics of equipment.

Sensors that have been embedded into a casting enable the detection, measurement, and evaluation of mechanical loads within the casting, such as compressive or tensile forces, deformations, or vibrations. Due to the production-orientated integration during the casting process, the sensors can be embedded precisely where the effects are experienced in the component, and are thus able to warn of an overloading of or damage to the casting for decision making. The CASTTRONICS® technology enables the embedding of strain sensors for condition monitoring as well as new concepts for lightweight design of castings made by aluminium high-pressure die-casting. The sensor functions using thick film technology – analogously to the classical strain gauge strip – through a change in the electrical resistance due to mechanical deformation. Thus, both dynamic load changes and static loads can be detected. A piezo thin-film sensor system has also been developed. These sensors are distinctive in that they can detect both dynamic and static loads without being elastically deformed themselves. 2D and 3D vision based sensors, ultrasonic sensors and other advanced sensors such as temperature and MEM sensor can also be applied to the Die Casting process.

For automotive and part supply industries, intelligent sensors can be applied within the overall production process to promote productivity with efficient resources and high quality and safety. From the photoelectric sensor to high-tech 3D vision systems, thin film MEM and ultrasonic and radar sensors, these sensor solutions help provide safe, fast and cost-effective production using smart senor unit and intelligent processing and actuators. These integrated intelligent sensor solutions monitor and optimise quality continuously in order to prevent machine failures and reduce downtime with fast conversion times, which directly increases productivity for industries.

CONCLUSIONS

Sensors and sensor intelligence has driven automation technology to change the world. As we embark on a new future with Industry 4.0. newly developed sensor technology and advanced communication (Internet of Things) will enhance the efficiency of manufacturing processes. Integrated intelligence into the devices, machines and the entire process will allow the development of the smart factory. In the case of the die casting manufacturing process, 2D and 3D vision based sensors, ultrasonic sensors and other advanced sensors such as temperature and MEM sensor are being applied; with embedded AI algorithms, these smart sensing technology will demonstrate the potential for developing smart die casting. These integrated technologies will provide the potential to improve the process efficiency, reduce scrap rate and save cost.

References

Albers, A., Gladysz, B. , Pinner, T., Butenko, V., Stürmlinger, T., (2016). Procedure for defining the system of objectives in the initial phase of an Industry 4.0 project focusing on intelligent quality control systems, Procedia CIRP 52-pp.262–267.

Bagheri, B., Yang, S., Kao, H.A., Lee, J., (2015). Cyber-physical systems architecture for self-aware machines in Industry 4.0 environment, IFAC-PapersOnLine 48 pp. 1622–1627.

Barua, S., Liou, F., Newkirk, J., Sparks, T., (2014). Vision-based defect detection in laser metal deposition process, Rapid Prototyp. J. 20 (1) 77–85

Bondar, S. , Hsu, J., Pfouga, A., Stiepandic, J., (2017). Agile digital transformation of system-of-systems architecture models using Zachman framework, J. Ind. Inf. Integr. . http://doi.org.proxy.lib.odu.edu/10.1016/j.jii.2017.03.001.

Castronic, Smart castings for Industry 4.0, (September 2018) Retrieved from https://www.ifam.fraunhofer.de/content/dam/ifam/en/documents/Shaping_Functional_Materials/casting_tec hnology/smart-casting-industry-4-0-fraunhofer-ifam.pdf

Casttronics, visited on 3 September 2018 https://www.ifam.fraunhofer.de/content/ dam/ifam/en/documents/Shaping_Functional_Materials/casting_technology/smart-casting-industry-4-0-fraunhofer-ifam.pdf

Everton, S K., Hirsch, M., Stravroulakis, P., Leach, R k., Clare, A. T., (2016) Review of in-situ process monitoring and in-situ metrology for metal additive manufacturing, Materials and Design 95: pp. 431–445

Georgakopoulos, D., Jayaraman, P.P., Fazia, M., Villari, M. , Ranjan, R., Internet of things and edge cloud computing roadmap for manufacturing, IEEE Cloud Comput. 3 (4) (2016) 66

Harrison, R., Vera, D., Ahmad, B., (2016). Engineering methods and tools for cyber—physical automation systems, Proc. IEEE 104 (5) pp. 973–985.

Kube, G., Rinn, T., (2015). Industry 4.0—the next revolution in the industrial sector, ZKG Int. 67, pp. 30–32.

Lee, J., Bagheri, B., Kao, H.A., (2015). A cyber-physical systems architecture for Industry 4.0-based manufacturing systems, Manuf. Lett. 3 pp. 18–23.

Leo, M., Medioni, G., Trivedi, M., Kanade, T., Farinella, G., (2017), Computer vision for assistive technologies, Computer Vision and Image Understanding, Volume 154, Pages 1-15

Li, X., Li, D., Wan, J., Vasilakos, A.V., Lai, C.F., Wang, S. (2015). A review of industrial wireless networks in the context of Industry 4.0, Wireless Networks pp. 1–19.

Lin, F., Chen, C., Zhang, N., Guan, X., Shen, X., (2016). Autonomous channel switching: towards efficient spectrum sharing for industrial wireless sensor networks, IEEE Internet Things J. 3 (2) pp. 231–243.

Mao, J., Zhou, Q., (2016) Sarmiento, M., A hybrid reader transceiver design for industrial internet of things, J. Ind. Inf. Integr. 2 (2016) 19–29. http://doi.org. proxy.lib.odu.edu/10.1016/j.jii.2016.05.001.

Pfeiffer, S., (2016). Industry 4.0 and humans, or why assembly work is more than routine work, Societies 6 - 16.

Roblek, V., Meško, M. Krapež, A., (2016). A complex view of Industry 4.0, SAGE Open 6

Schmidt, R., Möhring, M., Härting,R.C, Reichstein, C., Neumaier, P., Jozinovic´, P. ,(2015). Industry 4.0-potentials for creating smart products: empirical research results, in: International Conference on Business Information Systems, Springer International Publishing, pp. 16–27.

Seungin Shin, Min-Hyun Kim, Seibum B. Choi,(2016). Improving efficiency of ultrasonic distance sensors using pulse interval modulation, IEEE SENSORS.

Shafiq, S.I, Sanin, C., Szczerbicki, E., Toro, C., (2016). Virtual engineering factory: creating experience base for Industry 4.0, Cybern. Syst. Pp. 32–47.

Shafiq, S.I., Sanin,C., Toro, C., Szczerbicki, E., (2015). Virtual engineering object (VEO): toward experience-based design and manufacturing for Industry 4.0, Cybernic Syst. Pp. 35–50.

SICKinsight Magazine , Driving your industry 4WARD, www.sickinsight-online.com, visited 3 September 2018

SICKinsight Magazine, Simply reliable and simple efficient, www.sickinsight-online.com, visited 3 September 2018

Thames, L., Schaefer Software-defined cloud manufacturing for Industry 4.0, Procedia CIRP 52 (2016) 12–17.

Vogel-Heuser, B., D. Hess, Guest editorial Industry 4.0–prerequisites and visions, IEEE Trans. Autom. Sci. Eng. 13 (2) (2016) 411–413.

Wan, J., Tang, S., Shu, Z. , Li, D., Wang, S., Imran, M., Vasilakos, A., (2016) Software-de- fined industrial internet of things in the context of Industry 4.0, IEEE Sens. J. 16 (22) (2016) 7373–7380.

Yan, H., Xu, L., Bi, Z., Pang, Z., Zhang, J., Chen, Y., (2015). An emerging technology –wearable wireless sensor networks with applications in human health condi- tion monitoring, J. Manage. Anal. Pp. 121–137, doi: 10.1080/23270012. 2015.10295

Edge Analytics: Applying Machine Learning to Industrial IoT

Shadi Saleh Basurra and Mohamed Medhat Gaber

School of Computing and Digital Technology, Faculty of Computing, Engineering and the Built Environment, Birmingham City University,
Millennium Point, 1 Curzon Street, Birmingham, B4 7XG, UK
Email: {Shadi.Basurra, Mohamed.Gaber}@bcu.ac.uk

Abstract

The Internet of Things (IoT) continues to see a rapid growth in recent years, and the estimates suggest that its global market value will reach $457 billion by the year 2020. This exponential growth in IoT will drive economic growth and competitiveness in countries and companies, more specifically, in the areas of manufacturing, transportation and logistics. A typical IoT solution pipeline consists of five phases: 1) data capturing; 2) data normalisation and analytics; 3) management control and decision making; 4) data visualisation and 5) data storage. The second stage "data normalisation and analytics" is fundamental because during this stage the data will be inspected, and business decisions will later be made to improve the business flows. Machine Learning (ML) can play a critical role at this stage to make useful insights. Based on the live stream or historical data, ML can perform pattern recognition, facilitate intelligent decisions and forecast future performance with the objectives of reducing cost and increasing profitability. This chapter begins by discussing the difference between the three types of machine learning, namely supervised learning, unsupervised learning and reinforcement learning. It will later review the various IoT platforms that belong to either cloud based or edge based ML. Here, the advantages and the disadvantages of both types will be discussed, as well as the ideal project scenarios that can work for each type. Finally, this chapter will present some scenarios where applying machine learning to IoT can be used to optimise business operations, e.g. anomaly monitoring, predictive maintenance, performance optimization and transportation.

Keywords
Machine Learning, Internet of Things, Edge Analytics, Neural Networks.

INTRODUCTION

The rapid advancement in hardware technologies, processors and networking protocols made communication between different devices easier and robust. Looking to the future, Cisco IBSG predicts that around 50 billion device will be connected over the internet by the year 2020 Evans (2011). This trend has contributed to the revival of the concept of Internet of Things (IoT). IoT is a combination of embedded technologies, including sensors, and actuators that can be connected to the internet via physical wire or wirelessly Atzori et al. (2010).

This rapid expansion of IoT and its applications will generate enormous amounts of data that needs processing for optimising decision making. Due to the volume, variability and velocity of such data, there are various challenges in leveraging the vast amount of data. These challenges include the system capacity for storing and processing the data and and designing efficient and scalable algorithms to perform data analysis Fan and Bifet (2013). Data generated from IoT devices, e.g. at home from coffee machines, vehicles or fitness trackers, will need to be computationally analysed to reveal patterns, trends and associations – so we gain more insights about the data for informing conclusions and effective decision making. Machine learning (ML) provides the technical basis to extract useful information from the raw data generated by IoT. ML looks for patterns and structural description in the data which can be used to automate decision making. Unlike traditional computing where algorithms are configured explicitly with instructions to solve a problem, ML methods allow computers to learn from raw data and apply statistical analysis to perform an action based on a range of values. ML can also be used in forecasting what will happen in new situations from the data that describe events that happened in the past.

The recent advancements of ML have contributed to improvement of facial recognition systems, computer vision and helped in understanding natural languages Hussain *et al*. (2017). It is widely deployed in forensic computing for detecting credit card fraud Buczak and Guven (2016), and used to develop recommendation systems in the financial market. Moreover, there has been a growing interest in the medical sector for using ML for medical diagnosis. For example, Face2Gene app uses ML, via deep learning, to analyse facial dysmorphic features of patient phenotypes that correlate with rare genetic diseases. ML is not new, it has been around for a while but its applications have been restricted due to their complexity and high demand in computation power. One of the reasons for the current rise of ML is the evolution of cloud computing which offers high storage capabilities and high performance computing services. Due to the rapid advances in low-power and low-cost processors, IoT devices have now more computing power than computers from the early 2000s. For example, a Raspberry Pi can be a good representative of an IoT device. This will allow IoT to run lightweight machine learning at the edge (closer to the data source) to share the burden on the cloud, but also to avoid a single point of failure, minimise the network traffic, by conducting real-time analytics or filtering data on the IoT device Dickson (2018). Indeed the deployment of machine learning on the edge IoT is advantageous for many reasons:

Faster real-time prediction
Having machine learning performing prediction tasks including classification and regression on the edge, means it is close to the source of the sensor data, hence, it will reduce the time required if the prediction is performed on the cloud. For example, the data generated from self driving cars, for learning and prediction can reach up to 25 gigabytes per hour. If this data was to be sent to the cloud to perform data analysis, it will introduce huge delay that may also slow down its expected fast responsive manoeuvres or accelerating / breaking when dealing with sudden events on the road, which could potentially lead to serious accidents Ovenden (2018).

Increased operational reliability
With the possibility for storing and processing data, we can avoid issues related to connectivity with the cloud, hence, no single point of failure. This can benefit applications that require real-time processing and control such as audio and video, and for IoT devices deployed in places that suffer from weak / no internet access Ovenden (2018).

Increased security for the device and the data
Tracking and sensor data can generate highly sensitive information that could reveal the location and current activity of individuals and their health conditions. It is more secure to process this type of generated data locally. This will minimise the risk of sending raw data to the cloud as this may increase its vulnerability to various type of sniffing attacks Ovenden (2018), Abomhara and Køien (2015).

MACHINE LEARNING ALGORITHMS

ML algorithms are categorized based on how the learning is performed or how the feedback is given by the algorithms. Most machine learning methods can be categorised into three main categories supervised learning, unsupervised learning and reinforcement learning Sezer *et al*.

(2018). In supervised learning, the data are represented in vectors which pairs the input and the output values. These vectors have labelled features that define the meaning of the data. In supervised learning, the algorithm analyses the data, and produces an inferred function/model which is used to predict the outputs for given inputs. One problem that may result from the learning is known as overfitting. This is when the function works precisely with the training data but not for data outside the learning sample.

Unsupervised learning is typically used for large data which are unlabelled. In such circumstances, unsupervised learning techniques are used to understand the data, by making patterns or clusters through iterative processing without human intervention. This divides the data into regions or groups of features in order to be labelled so that they can be used by supervised learning algorithms, or can be used for data exploration and description.

Reinforcement learning is where an agent learns how to behave in an environment by performing actions and observing the results. At the beginning, the agent is not configured with which action to take at particular circumstances, as in most forms of machine learning, but instead must discover the actions that lead to the highest reward by trying them. This will require trial-and-error search and delayed reward which are vital elements of reinforcement learning Sutton et al. (1998).

Supervised learning algorithms

Linear Regression

Linear regression is commonly used in statistics, and is a key algorithm in ML. It helps to generate models for understanding the relationship between input X (also known as independent variable) and the output Y (dependent variable), where X and Y are both numerical variables. It is called a simple regression, if there is only one independent X and one dependent variable Y , and is called multiple regression when they are multiple independent variables influencing one Y dependent variable. Linear regression focuses on minimising the error to make accurate predictions whenever possible. Linear regression relationship is represented as a line that best fits the relationship between X and Y Yan and Su (2009). However, linear regression is limited to linear relationships, hence, it does not show good performance to model curved relationships such as the curved correlation between income and the age. Moreover, it is prone to overfitting, this is when the model gets over trained by including the noise and inaccurate data entries in the data sets Hoskuldsson (1988). In this case, the overfit model becomes too complicated and may work well with high accuracy with the learned data sets, but it is unlikely to work with new data sets. Simple linear regression is represented in the equation $Y = a * X + b$ where Y is dependent variable, a is the slope, X is independent variable and b is the intersection point on the Y axis of a *2d* graph.

Logistic Regression

Logistic Regression is used for classification. In contrary to linear regression, discussed above, which predicts the value based on a given set of inputs, logistic regression tries to find a relationship between features and the probability of the inputs of belonging to a specific class. For example, given the number of hours spent by a student studying for the exam, logistic regression can predict if the student passes or fails the exam. This example depicts a Binomial Logistic Regression where the output predicted value can be either true or false Tripepi et al. (2008). If the regression analysis required to deal with more than two outcomes, Multinomial Logistic Regression is used to predict the probability of category membership of a dependant variable based on multiple independent variables Bentler and Weeks (1980). In logistic regression, the data points on the solution space cannot be fitted within a straight line like linear regression, instead they are mapped using a Sigmoid function that looks like an 'S' (See Figure 1). Logistic regression is fast, and requires less computation power. It is used to understand the effect of predictor variables on the outcome. However, logistic regression does not capture complex relationships e.g. non-linear problems as its decision is linear Tu (1996).

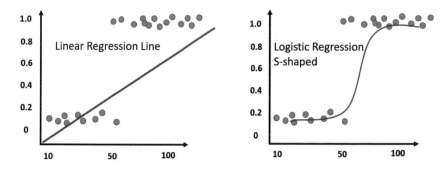

FIGURE 1: Random Forest Simplified Representation Yazici et al. (2018)

SVM

Support Vector Machines (SVM) is a supervised learning method, and can be applied to classification or regression problems. SVM is built on the concept of decision boundaries. In a two dimensional space, SVM defines a hyperplane that splits the solution space into two parts which differentiate the two classes. This is called linear classifier as it separates a set of data into their respective category Vapnik (1982). In more complex scenarios, the data cannot be separated with a linear hyperplane, hence a complex hyperplane is used instead to optimally separate the two classes, applying a data transformation using a kernel function. Accelerating the process, using what is known as 'kernel trick', allows the transformation tobe applied to very large spaces Zhu and Blumberg (2002). In a large solution space, some solutions of different classes can overlap. A perfect classification will attempt to separate both using a perfect partitioning, however, this risks overfitting. Regularization algorithms are used to avoid overfitting using non linear classification with reasonable accuracy and speed. One of the main challenges with SVM is determining the values given for the regularisation and the kernel parameters, which are sensitive to overfitting Cawley and Talbot (2010).

k-NN

Despite its simplicity to run and implement, k-NN can perform classification with reasonable accuracy on complex data sets. k-NN measures the distance from a new data point to all other training data points. Using Euclidean or Manhattan functions, it selects the nearest points based on the parameter k - usually a small positive integer value that is responsible in the selection of the neighbourhood size. Using majority voting, this new data point will be assigned the class that is most common among its k nearest neighbours Short and Fukunaga (1981). k-NN is robust when used on large and noisy training data sets. It is a non-parametric method, thus is used heavily for pattern recognition problems, as it can handle multi-class cases Weinberger and Saul (2009). However, it is hard to determine the optimal value of the k parameter Deekshatulu *et al.* (2013). Moreover, k-NN is computationally expensive, as the algorithm will need to compute the distance from the data point to all training data points in the solution space Liao *et al.* (2001).

Random Forest

Random Forest is another popular ML algorithm which can be used for regression and classification. Here, multiple samples of the training data are selected and this method generates what is called bootstrap datasets. From these bootstrap samples, the algorithm constructs decision trees. At each step, the algorithm randomly selects a subset of features to grow the trees with decision nodes. This process will repeat in making new bootstrapped datasets and building new trees. This process generates a wide variety of decision trees for the same datasets. The results are combined and either averaged for predicting values such as sale volumes, or a voting mechanism is used to predict the output for classification outcome such as classification of papers as public or confidential Liaw *et al.* (2002).

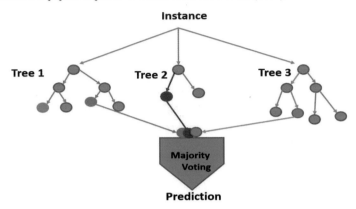

FIGURE 2: Random Forest Simplified Representation Yazici *et al.* (2018)

The main advantages of the Random Forest algorithm is that it works well with high dimensionality data sets, and it can cope well with missing values while maintaining reasonable prediction accuracy. On the other hand, since prediction is calculated based on the mean, Random Forest can lack precision when used for regression Biau and Scornet (2016).

Neural networks

Neural networks are one of the main tools in machine learning. It is inspired by how the human brain works. The human brain consists of neurons that are connected to form a network of neurons. These neurons are responsible for processing and passing the electrical impulses received from our senses – so the brain can interpret them correctly Hinton (1992).

The basic unit of neural networks is an artificial neuron, typically called a node in a layer. The neural network consist of three types of nodes according to the layer the node is in: input node, hidden node and output node. There is no computation performed at the input node as the job of these nodes is to only transform the information from external sources to the hidden nodes. The hidden nodes are responsible for processing the inputs during which they are associated with weight w parameters which are trainable to control the influence and the direction of its output. The hidden nodes apply a function on the weighted sum of its inputs

$$f(w1 \times x1 + w2 \times x2 \ldots + b)$$

where *x1* and *x2* are inputs provided by the input node, *w1* and *w2* are weights associated by the hidden nodes to the inputs *x1* and *x2*. b is the bias which is used to adjust the output along with the weighted sum to produce a desired output during the learning phase. The weighted sum of a hidden node is then passed through an activation function to produce the output of the node. The computation results performed on the hidden nodes are finally passed to the output node which uses an activation function, e.g. linear for regression and Softmax for classification problems Tu (1996).

Deep neural network (DNN) is an artificial neural network with multiple hidden layers in between the input and output nodes. DNN techniques learn categories incrementally through its hidden nodes. In this case, a DNN defines abstract features before it defines the low level – specific- features. For example, in identifying risks of developing breast cancer in individuals, hidden nodes

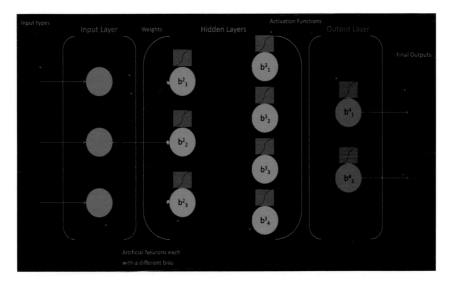

FIGURE 3: The figure depicts an Artificial Neural Network Yazici *et al.* (2018)

first look at the general categories such as age and number of children, and later deeper hidden nodes will look at more specific features such as family history and hormonal disorders Furundzic et al. (1998). Deep neural network required training to adjust the weights and the B parameters in order to reduce the error between the outputs and the training data sets, hence, a backpropagation technique is used. It uses an error function with respect to the weights to understand relationships between the inputs and outputs.

The calculation of the gradients moves backwards, which means that the weights of the last nodes are calculated first, then the first weights associated with the first node are calculated last Hinton (2007). Neural networks are easy to train, and can be developed using multiple training algorithms. Research showed that they can identify complex patterns and relationships between independent and dependant variables. However, these capabilities come at other expenses. ANN requires high computation power, but more importantly it is a black box which might produce correct prediction, but can not provide an explanation of why and how. It can also be time consuming as building the network structure does not follow any rules, and is usually obtained through experience and trial and error Tu (1996).

Unsupervised learning algorithms

K-means
k-means is one of the simplest unsupervised learning algorithm. It is used to define groups in data based on instance similarity. The algorithm iteratively assigns each data point to one of k groups/clusters based on the given features. The algorithm starts by identifying random k centres, one for each cluster, which will later be used to label new data instances/examples. The location of cluster centres (known as centroids) is critical as it leads to different results, hence, it is ideal to initially maximise the distance between the centroids as much as possible for optimal results. After identifying the group centroid, using the Euclidean distance function the algorithm will iteratively assigns each point to its nearest group centroid. Finally, once all data points are assigned to a cluster group, the algorithm will search for better centroids to replace the current ones by selecting better cluster members to act as the cluster centroid for each cluster. This is done by calculating the mean of all values in the cluster to select an optimal a new centroid. Centroids will continue move, and due to change in distance between the new centroid and the cluster members, new members will be added or released to/from the newly forming cluster of the centroid, and this will continue until the k-means algorithm is converged (i.e. when no member can replace the current centroid in the cluster) Kanungo et al. (2002).

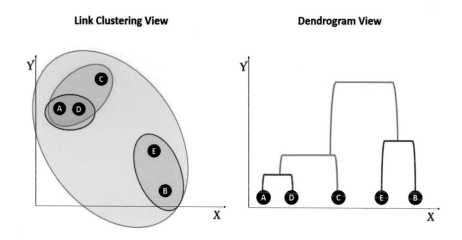

FIGURE 4: Hierarchical Clustering with Dendrogram Visualisation Yazici *et al.* (2018)

The algorithm is fast and robust. The algorithm works well if the data are distinct, and the data sets of a low density, i.e. separated from each other. However, one of the main issue of the k-means algorithm is defining the optimal number of centroids in advance, hence, there will be a trial and error process until the optimal number is found. Also, the algorithm does not handle non-linear data sets well Hamerly and Elkan (2004).

Hierarchical clustering – Agglomerative
Hierarchical clustering is a simple algorithm that partitions the data points into groups. Once the algorithm is initiated, each data point is considered as a cluster on its own. The algorithm computes the distances between the clusters with the aim to merge the clusters into bigger cluster. This process continues until the entire data set is encapsulated by one single cluster.

The output of the algorithm is known as a dendrogram (See Fig. 4), which is represented as a tree of linked nodes. This illustrates the resulted merged clusters, but more importantly acts as a trace that shows when the merging was established for each cluster throughout the process Johnson (1967). The nodes are arranged in accordance with their similarity factor, hence, nodes that have the same linkage heights are similar, and those with different heights are dissimilar. Merging of clusters is performed using three common methods Yim and Ramdeen (2015) as follows. *Single linkage*: In each step, the algorithm merges the clusters of two pairs that depict the smallest distance between them. This type of clustering produces minimal spanning trees, and premature merging of clusters which are vastly dissimilar. *Complete linkage*: the algorithm merges two clusters that have the furthest distance showing huge dissimilarity. This prevents creating extended clusters. *Average linkage*: is clustering based on the average distances of all pairs of the clusters subject for merging. The main advantages of hierarchical clustering is that the Dendograms are a good visualization aid in providing hierarchical relations between clusters, and it is easy to implement, however, experimental research Steinbach et al. (2000) showed that other clustering mechanisms can outperform hierarchical clustering e.g. k-means clustering.

Reinforcement learning

Reinforcement learning is a type of machine learning that uses various reward feedback mechanisms so that an agent software or machine learns from the environment it resides in to achieve an ideal behaviour, but also to maximise its performance. There are three main concepts of reinforcement learning: state, action and reward. If we consider a robot learning how to move using reinforcement learning, the state describes the current situation, or the position of the robot. The action is what the robot can do at each state in order to reach another state while maximising the reward. For example, a robot can move 5 meters toward the north direction which leads to a dead-end, or moves 15 meters toward the south direction without being exposed to any barrier. From previous moves, the robot understands that hitting into a wall will get negative reward 'depicting punishment', thus, it chooses to move south as it is maximises its reward Kaelbling et al. (1996), Zhang et al. (2017).

Q-learning

Q-learning is a reinforcement learning method which is used to help the agent to learn a policy which determines what action to execute under what circumstances. Q-learning does not require to construct a model of the environment, and works by keeping a table with all possible states and actions that can be performed on these states. Each row represents a state S and and an action A that an agent can execute associated with a Q value that depicts the reward R that would be gained if this action is executed by the agent.

$$Q : S \times A -> R$$

At the beginning, the Q values are initialised with predefined random values, however, they will later be updated based on the experience given the obtained rewards from the selected action. Through the value iteration update, the algorithm gives a better approximation of the Q value for an action using the weighted average of the old value and the new information Sutton et al. (1998). However, Q-learning seems to take a long time to reach the optimal value even in normal circumstances, since iterations will have to be performed before a negative score is awarded Manju and Punithavalli (2011)

EDGE-IOT USE CASES

Machine learning and IoT have experienced a boost in popularity among industrial companies thanks to the rise of the IoT platforms that supports ML. Many companies are already designating IoT as a strategically significant area, while others have kicked off pilot projects to map the potential of IoT in business operations. The following are use cases where the integration between IoT and ML can create new business opportunities helping business growth.

Anomaly monitoring

Constant monitoring of fast machines and systems in search for errors is difficult, and may not be free of mistakes. Today, most anomaly detection systems are reactive, hence, even if errors are detected, it will be after the occurrence of the error. For example, in factories, if a defect is detected, the production line would have already produced malfunctioning items, resulting into wasting raw materials, energy and time. Hence, the timing in detecting this error is critical. In an ideal world, anomaly detection should provide warning before the occurrence of the errors, although it is hard to achieve, but if ML is used to learn from the system behaviour, patterns and historical operational errors to offer a better anomaly detection mechanism, it will provide huge operational benefits in many areas.

Industrial predictive maintenance

Acme Industries, well known for manufacturing high precision drill bushings, uses Google Cloud Machine learning and Losant IoT platform to monitor and predict the health of the Acme facilities. This can be done using data visualisation and alert generation with the aim to minimise production time and increase operational efficiencies to reduce the overall manufacturing cost. Accelerometers (vibration sensors) along with temperature sensors will be attached to each of the machines to sense and process vibration data. Sensors can send data to the cloud for *training* using Google ML Engine which supports TensorFlow, but *prediction*, using a neural network model, happens at the edges where alerts can be raised or control of the machine to switching on / off. This way we can monitor but also detect the health of the entire facility. These vibration/temperature models can decide if the machine is operating correctly, or if it is likely to be experiencing failure Foxworth (2017).

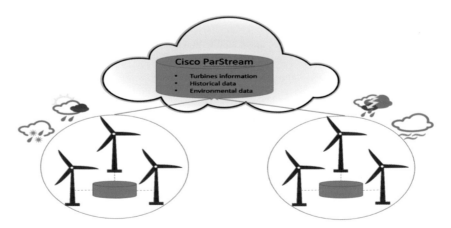

FIGURE 5: Data about weather, location and prices adds context value to turbine data. The system keeps granular data at the wind turbine for inspection, and aggregated data is stored at the cloud using the ParStream which update these data every minute.

Performance optimization

Envision Energy, the largest Chinese offshore wind turbine supplier, is considering edge analytics to optimise their wind turbines' performance. To reduce turbine downtime, Cisco has proposed the use of machine learning such as linear regression and neural networks to predict the weather ahead of time in order to quickly adjust its positioning or blades' direction to respond to the continuous changes in environmental factors such as wind direction, wind speed and temperature. Using Cisco ParStream for real-time analytics in IoT, Envision can monitor their 20,000 wind turbines, each fitted with 150 sensors, in real time (See Figure 5). Historical analysis can also be used for predictive maintenance for the turbines which are often located in remote locations, where it can be hard to send engineers out for on-site inspection on a regular basis. According to Cisco, using edge enalytics could improve the productivity of the wind turbines by 15% while minimising downtime, which will lead to $158M of economic profit Ruland (2016).

Driverless cars

Direverless cars have become a reality and are currently being produced by various manufacturers, for example Tesla and Uber. Self-driving cars are made for human comfort, convenience and safety. According to the U.S. National Highway Traffic Safety Administration (NHTSA) automated driving is safer as 90% of car crashes are caused by human errors, hence, automating driving could dramatically improve this figure. Deep reinforcement learning such as the Q-Learning method can be used to train the car for efficient acceleration and breaking Gu *et al.* (2016). AI-enabled IoT connected to car parts can detect the possibility of component failure, hence, it could fire an order at the dealership to resolve the issue, and guarantee that the replacement is in store before the failure becomes imminent. Using ML, the car can drive itself home after being repaired.

CONCLUSIONS

The rapid enhancement in technologies made communication between devices easier, and hence around 50 billion devices will be connected by 2020. This contributed to the revival of embedded devices that combine various sensors and actuators and are known as IoT. This growth will generate an enormous amount of data that needs processing for decision making. ML provides the technical means to extract and learn from the data to provide for effective decision making and control. Deploying ML on the cloud was never feasible due to their high demand for memory and computing power, however, with the new advancement in IoT, some have more computing power than computers made in the early 2000s. Deploying ML on IoT has tremendous advantages including real-time prediction, increasing security and operation reliability as there is no need to communicate with the cloud over the internet. Machine Learning methodologies like Deep Learning (DL) and Reinforcement Learning (RL) and their combinations demonstrate unprecedented performance in a wide range of applications such as anomaly monitoring, predictive maintenance, automated decision making and control.

With the rapid growth in IoT which is estimated to reach $457 billion by 2020, major software/hardware companies are racing to lead this new market. Amazon launched AWS Greengrass in the market in 2016 taking advantage of the rich AWS Lambda ecosystem. Microsoft released Azure IoT Edge which supports container-based modules for deployment, and supports major programming languages. Unlike the previous two platforms, Google released their Cloud IoT Edge in 2018, which is an integration between Google's Cloud TPU and Cloud IOT offering a complete cloud to edge solution including software and hardware Google (2018). Moreover, IBM enhanced its Watson IoT platform which manages IoT devices securely and efficiently, where its IoT Gateways can act as a mini server to run lightweight ML algorithms IBM(2018).

The fast enhancement in IoT hardware in terms of processing and storage capacity allowed IoT to run on lightweight IoT device. However, most perform the inference on the IoT device, while the learning still happens on the cloud due to the algorithm's high demand for processing power and storage capacity which none of the aforementioned platforms or devices can offer. The future direction would be to maintain IoT devices' autonomy and distribution to avoid a single point of failure, and to further enhance security from any interference / cyber attacks utilising security gaps in the communication protocols/networks between the device and the cloud. More attention should go towards making ML more lightweight. For example, the learning or parts of the learning should occur on the IoT device itself to reduce the dependence on network connectivity and cloud capability which is also useful when IoT-AI is deployed in remote areas such as forests, agricultural areas and conflict zones in developing countries and oil exploration areas in deserts and seas.

References

Abdallah, F., Basurra, S., & Gaber, M. 2017, A hybrid agent-based and probabilistic model for fine-grained behavioural energy waste simulation. 29 IEEE International Conference on Tools with Artificial Intelligence (ICTAI), Boston, USA.

Abomhara, M. & Køien, G., M., 2015. Cyber security and the internet of things: vulnerabilities, threats, intruders and attacks. Journal of Cyber Security, 4(1):65–88.

IBM, About watson IoT platform, Feb 2018. URL https://console.bluemix.net/docs/services/ IoT/iotplatform_overview.html#about_iotplatform.

Atzori, L., Iera, A. & Morabito, G., 2010. The internet of things: A survey.

Computer Networks, 54(15):2787 – 2805, 2010. ISSN 1389-1286. doi: https://doi.org/ 10.1016/j.comnet.2010.05.010. URL http://www.sciencedirect.com/science/article/pii/ S1389128610001568.

AWS Greengrass - Amazon Web Services. URL https://aws.amazon.com/greengrass/.

Bentler, P., M. & Weeks, D., W., 1980. Linear structural equations with latent variables. Psychome- trika, 45(3):289–308.

Biau, G. & Scornet, E., 2014. A random forest guided tour. Test, 25(2):197–227, 2016.

Buczak, A., L., & Guven, E., 2016. A survey of data mining and machine learning methods for cy- ber security intrusion detection. IEEE Communications Surveys Tutorials, 18(2):1153–1176, Secondquarter 2016. ISSN 1553-877X. doi: 10.1109/COMST.2015.2494502.

Cawley, G., C., & Talbot, N., LC, 2010. On over-fitting in model selection and subsequent selection bias in performance evaluation. Journal of Machine Learning Research, 11(Jul):2079–2107, 2010.

Deekshatulu, B., L., 2013. Priti Chandra, et al. Classification of heart disease using k-nearest neighbour and genetic algorithm. Procedia Technology, 10:85–94, 2013.

DICKSON, B., 2018. When the cloud is swamped, it's edge computing, AI to the rescue, April 2018. URL https://uk.pcmag.com/google-photos-for-web/94303/feature/ when-the-cloud-is-swamped-its-edge-computing-ai-to-the-rescu. (Online; Accessed on 19-August-2018).

Edge tpu - run inference at the edge. URL https://cloud.google.com/edge-tpu/.

European Commission. European commission directive 2010/31/eu on 19 may 2010 on the en- ergy performance of buildings. Technical Report 35, European Parliament and of the Council, 2010. URL http://eur-lex.europa.eu/legal-content/en/TXT/uri=CELEX:32010L0031

Evans, D., 2011. The internet of things: How the next evolution of the internet is changing everything.

CISCO white paper, 1(2011):1–11, 2011.

Face2gene uses facial recognition tech to aid diagnosis of rare diseases. Biometric Technology Today, 2017(4):12, 2017. ISSN 0969-4765. doi: https://doi.org/10.1016/S0969-4765(17)30078-4.

URL http://www.sciencedirect.com/science/article/pii/S0969476517300784.

Fan, W. & Bifet, A., 2013. Mining big data: Current status, and forecast to the future. SIGKDD Explor. Newsl., 14(2):1–5. ISSN 1931-0145. doi: 10.1145/2481244.2481246. URL http://doi.acm.org/10.1145/2481244.2481246.

Foxworth, T, 2017. Using iot and machine learning for industrial predictive maintenance. URL https://www.losant.com/blog/ using-iot-and-machine-learning-for-industrial-predictive-maintenance.

Ruland, T. 2016. Edge Analytics: Use Cases for Industry 4.0, Data and Analytics Group, Cisco, pp 21-23 (28). URL https://pdfs.semanticscholar.org/presentation/1835/161c4f81ef92cb7d68a9c17d1786a20c4b47.pdf

Furundzic, D., Djordjevic, M., & Bekic, A., J., 1998. Neural networks approach to early breast cancer detection. Journal of Systems Architecture, 44(8):617 – 633, ISSN 1383- 7621. doi: https://doi.org/10.1016/S1383-7621(97)00067-2. URL http://www.sciencedirect. com/science/article/pii/S1383762197000672.

Gaber, M., Aneiba, A., Basurra, S., S., Batty, O., Elmisery, A., Ko-valchuk, Y. & Ur Rehman, M., H., 2018. Internet of things and data mining (2018): From applications to techniques and systems. WIREs Data Mining and Knowledge Discovery. Accepted for publication.

Gremban, K. 2018. What is azure IoT Edge. URL https://docs.microsoft.com/en-us/ azure/iot-edge/about-iot-edge.

Gu, S., Lillicrap, T., Sutskever, I. & Levine, S, 2016. Continuous deep q-learning with model-based acceleration. In International Conference on Machine Learning, pages 2829– 2838.

Hamerly, G. & Elkan, C., 2004.Learning the k in k-means. In Advances in neural information processing systems, pages 281–288.

Hinton, G., E., 1992. How neural networks learn from experience. Scientific American, 267(3): 144–151.

Hinton, G., E., 2007. Learning multiple layers of representation. Trends in Cognitive Sciences, 11 (10):428 – 434, 2007. ISSN 1364-6613. doi: https://doi.org/10.1016/j.tics.2007.09.004. URL http://www.sciencedirect.com/science/article/pii/S1364661307002173.

Hoskuldsson, A., 2008. Classification and regression by random forest. Journal of Chemometrics, 22 (3-4):150– 177. doi: 10.1002/cem.1131. URL https://onlinelibrary.wiley.com/doi/abs/ 10.1002/cem.1131.

Hussain, T., Siniscalchi, S., M., Lee, C., Wang, S., Tsao, Y. & Liao, W. 2017. Experimental study on extreme learning machine applications for speech enhancement. IEEE Access, 5:25542–25554. ISSN 2169-3536. doi: 10.1109/ACCESS.2017.2766675.

Hwang, Y., 2018. Ml and IoT in the battle for the edge. URL https://www.leverege. com/blogpost/ml-iot-edge-computing.

Janakiram MSV. 5 reasons why azure iot edge is industry's most promising edge computing platform, Jul 2018. URL https://www.forbes.com/sites/janakirammsv/2018/07/01/5-reasons-why-azure-iot-edge-is-industrys-most-promising-edge-computing-platform/#1615f01a3249.

Johnson, S. C, 1967. Hierarchical clustering schemes. Psychometrika, 32(3):241–254, 1967.

Kaelbling, L., P., & Littman, M., L., 1996. and Andrew W Moore. Reinforcement learning: A survey. Journal of artificial intelligence research, 4:237–285.

Kanungo, T., Mount, D., M., Netanyahu, N. S., Piatko, C., D., Silverman, R. & Wu, A., Y, 2002. An efficient k-means clustering algorithm: analysis and implementation. IEEE Transactions on Pattern Analysis and Machine Intelligence, 24(7):881–892, July 2002. ISSN 0162-8828. doi: 10.1109/TPAMI.2002.1017616.

Kienzler, R, 2018. Build a cognitive iot app in just 7 steps, Aug 2018. URL https://www.ibm. com/developerworks/library/iot-cognitive-iot-app-machine-learning/index.html.

Liao, S., Lopez, M. A. & Leutenegger, S., T., 2001. High dimensional similarity search with space filling curves. In Proceedings 17th International Conference on Data Engineering, pages 615–622. doi: 10.1109/ICDE.2001.914876.

Liaw, A. & Wiener, M., et al, 2002. Classification and regression by random forest. R news, 2(3): 18–22, 2002.

Mahdavinejad, M., S. & Rezvan, M., Barekatain, M., Adibi, P., Barnaghi, P. & Sheth, A., P, 2017. Machine learning for internet of things data analysis: a survey. Digital Communications and Networks, 4(3):161 – 175. ISSN 2352-8648. doi: https://doi.org/10.1016/j.dcan.2017.10.002. URL http://www.sciencedirect.com/science/ article/pii/S235286481730247X.

Manju, S. & Punithavalli, 2011. M. An analysis of q-learning algorithms with strategies of reward function. International Journal on Computer Science and Engineering, 3(2):814–820.

Manyika, J., Chui, M., Bisson, P., Woetzel, J., Dobbs, R., Bughin, J. & Aharon, D., 2015. The internet of things: mapping the value beyond the hype. Pages 1–24. McKinsey & Company. URL https://www.mckinsey.com/~/media/McKinsey/ Business%20Functions/McKinsey%20Digital/Our%20Insights/The%20Internet%20of% 20Things%20The%20value%20of%20digitizing%20the%20physical%20world/Unlocking_ the_potential_of_the_Internet_of_Things_Executive_summary.ashx.

Mittal, A., K., & Bhandari, D., 2013. A novel approach to implement green wave system and detection of stolen vehicles. In 2013 3rd IEEE International Advance Computing Conference (IACC), pages 1055–1059, doi: 10.1109/IAdCC.2013.6514372.

Nellore, K. & Hancke, G., P., 2016. Traffic management for emergency vehicle priority based on visual sensing. Sensors, 16(11), 11 2016. ISSN 1424-8220. doi: 10.3390/s16111892.

Ovenden, J. 2018. Edge computing and the future of machine learning. URL https://channels.theinnovationenterprise.com/articles/ why-machine-learning-needs-edge-computing.

Perez-Lombard, L., Ortiz, J. & Pout, C., 2008. A review on buildings energy consumption information. Energy and Buildings, 40(3):394 – 398, ISSN 0378-7788. doi: https://doi. org/10.1016/j.enbuild.2007.03.007. URL http://www.sciencedirect.com/science/article/ pii/S0378778807001016.

Polson, N., G. & Sokolov, V., O, 2017. Deep learning for short-term traffic flow prediction. Transportation Research Part C: Emerging Technologies, 79:1–17, 2017.

Sezer, O., B., Dogdu, E. & Ozbayoglu, A., M., 2018. Context-aware computing, learning, and big data in internet of things: A survey. IEEE Internet of Things Journal, 5(1):1–27. ISSN 2327-4662. doi: 10.1109/JIOT.2017.2773600.

Short, R. & Fukunaga, K, 1981. The optimal distance measure for nearest neighbor classification. IEEE Transactions on Information Theory, 27(5):622–627. ISSN 0018-9448. doi: 10.1109/TIT.1981.1056403.

Steinbach, M., Karypis, G., Kumar, V., 2000. A comparison of document clustering techniques. In KDD workshop on text mining, volume 400, pages 525–526. Boston.

Sundar, R., Hebbar, S. & Golla, V., 2015. Implementing intelligent traffic control system for congestion control, ambulance clearance, and stolen vehicle detection. IEEE Sensors Journal, 15(2):1109– 1113. ISSN 1530-437X. doi: 10.1109/JSEN.2014.2360288.

Sutton, R., S., Barto, A., G., 1998. Reinforcement learning: An introduction. MIT press, 1998.

Tripepi, G., Jager, K., J., Dekker, F., W., & Zoccali, C., 2018. Linear and logistic regression analysis. Kidney International, 73(7):806 – 810, ISSN 0085-2538. doi: https://doi.org/10.1038/sj.ki. 5002787. URL http://www.sciencedirect.com/science/article/pii/S0085253815530895.

Tu, J., V., 1996. Advantages and disadvantages of using artificial neural networks versus logistic regression for predicting medical outcomes. Journal of Clinical Epidemiology, 49(11):1225– 1231. ISSN 0895-4356. doi:

https://doi.org/10.1016/S0895-4356(96)00002-9.   URL
http://www.sciencedirect.com/science/article/pii/S0895435696000029.

Turakhia, C., 2017. Engineering more reliable transportation with machine learning and AI at Uber,. URL
https://eng.uber.com/machine-learning/.

Vapnik, V., 1982. Estimation of Dependences Based on Empirical Data: Springer Series in Statistics, Springer-
Verlag, Berlin, Heidelberg. ISBN 0387907335.

Weinberger, K., Q. & Saul, L., K., S., 2009. Lawrence K Saul. Distance metric learning for large margin nearest
neighbor classification. Journal of Machine Learning Research, 10(Feb):207–244.

Williams, C., 2011. Google unwraps its gateway drug: Edge tpu chips for iot ai code, Jul 2018. URL
https://www.theregister.co.uk/2018/07/25/google_edge_tpu_chip/.

Yan, X. & Su, X., G., 2009. Linear Regression Analysis: Theory and Computing. World Scientific Publishing
Co., Inc., River Edge, NJ, USA, 2009. ISBN 9789812834102, 9812834109.

Yazici, M., T. & Basurra, S., S., & Gaber, M., M., 2018, Edge machine learning: Enabling smart internet of things
applications. Big Data and Cognitive Computing, 2(3), 2018. ISSN 2504-2289. doi: 10.3390/bdcc2030026.
URL http://www.mdpi.com/2504-2289/2/3/26.

Yim, O. & Ramdeen, K., T., 2015. Hierarchical cluster analysis: comparison of three linkage measuresand
application to psychological data. The quantitative methods for psychology, 11(1): 8–21.

Zavitsas, K., & Kaparias, I. & Conduits, M., G., H., B., 2010. Coordination of network descriptors for urban
intelligent transport systems. Technical Report 11, Imperial College London, The address of the publisher.

Zhang, J., Springenberg, J., T., Boedecker, J., and Burgard, W., 2017. Deep re- inforcement learning with
successor features for navigation across similar environments. In Intelligent Robots and Systems (IROS), 2017
IEEE/RSJ International Conference on, pages 2371–2378.

Zhang, Y., He, C., Tang, B. & Wei, Y., 2015. China's energy consumption in the building sector: A life cycle
approach. Energy and Buildings, 94(Supplement C):240 – 251, 2015. ISSN 0378-7788. doi:
https://doi.org/10.1016/j.enbuild.2015.03.011.   URL
http://www.sciencedirect.com/science/article/pii/S0378778815002030.

Zhao, D., McCoy, A., P., Du, J., Agee, P. & Lu., Y, 2017. Interaction effects of building technology and resident
behavior on energy consumption in residential buildings. Energy and Buildings, 134 (Supplement C):223 –
233.   ISSN   0378-7788.   doi: https://doi.org/   10.1016/j.enbuild.2016.10.049.   URL
http://www.sciencedirect.com/science/article/pii/ S0378778816313718.

Zhu, G. & Blumberg, D., G., Classification using aster data and svm algorithms; The case study of beer sheva,
israel. Remote Sensing of Environment, 80(2):233 – 240, 2002. ISSN 0034- 4257. doi:
https://doi.org/10.1016/S0034-4257(01)00305-4.   URL   http://www.sciencedirect.
com/science/article/pii/S0034425701003054.

Parallel Processing of Big Data in the Automotive Industry

Roger Tait

School of Computing & Digital Technology, Birmingham City University,
Millennium Point, Birmingham, UK. B4 7AP.
Email: roger.tait@bcu.ac.uk

Abstract

In recent times, big data and associated analytics has caught the attention of manufacturers who wish to optimise their production lines. Due to the relentless march of automation the amount of data generated in the manufacturing industries is growing at an exponential rate. Production lines which once spoke to the ether now bristle with sensors collecting and transmitting data ripe for analysis. Traditionally, research into the analysis of large data sets has been focused on fields such as machine learning, data mining and knowledge management. These and other research trends are now finding practical application in manufacturing domains where data is a commodity bursting with potential. As with any learning process the more you know about a system the more accurate the predictions you can make about future trends. Hidden insights into the relationship between process and value are now emerging from big data sets helping inform strategic decisions. By accurately modelling every eventuality, manufacturers can optimize the use of their machines and deploy resources more efficiently. Once finished, products that contain numerous sensors are feeding back into the manufacturing process adding to the data deluge. In this paper, generic parallel processing of large data sets is introduced and its suitability for deployment in the automotive manufacturing industry is considered.

Keywords
Automotive Manufacturing, Parallel Processing, Data Distribution.

INTRODUCTION

The emergence of big data sets, such as those in automotive manufacturing, coupled with complex algorithms have increased the demand for high speed processing capabilities (Eastwood 2017). The use of parallel processing to overcome time constraints associated with applications is growing in popularity. Conveniently, many of the algorithms used in manufacturing are inherently parallel and are therefore well suited to a distributed implementation. An important consideration when adopting a parallel processing approach is the architecture of the host system (Englander 2009). In a system constructed of a single machine with multiple processors, data distribution is not required, these systems are viewed as a tightly-coupled architecture. A loosely-coupled system, in contrast, consisting of multiple computers in different locations will require its own distribution, communication and accumulation mechanisms. When a distribution scheme is employed, information regarding size of the original data and the identity of the processor allocated to it are just some of the additional information normally required to accompany partitioned data.

In a loosely-coupled architecture parallel processing consists of three main steps: data distribution, local processing and processed data accumulation. Distribution is the process of dividing data into segments each of which is then assigned to a unique process. Under a duplicate distribution scheme each process is sent an exact copy of the original data; this represents the simplest approach. An alternative more complex scheme can also be adopted where the data is divided into variable sized segments (Nicolescu & Jonker 2000). Once distributed, each process applies local processing to its allocated segment. When data allocated to other processes are required, it can be transferred by inter-process communication. Finally, after application of the parallel algorithm, distributed processed data are accumulated and combined. Due to the variety of algorithms developed, variations are most apparent in the local processing step of many parallel processing frameworks.

Seinstra and colleagues (Seinstra *et al* 2002) describe how inter-process communications can be categorised into groups based on their pattern of data access. These patterns also represent a strategy for synchronisation between communicating processors. One-to-one access is common in functionality such as subtraction and multiplication, where the value of an output maps directly to the input. Alternatively, a one-to-many relationship exists in neighbourhood operators which calculate an output based on a function of the input's immediate neighbourhood. Naturally, the handling and transmission of non-contiguous data differs from data stored as contiguous blocks. Data stored randomly in memory causes additional overheads due to the need for packing into a contiguous buffer before transmission.

There is a multitude of data available to support the automotive industry to help them understand their customers and the products they manufacture (Lorica 2017). The sheer scale and complexity of useful data limits manufacturers in their ability to analyse this effectively and act on findings. This is not due to difficulties associated with data collection, but the specialist knowledge required to process the data in a timely fashion. In this paper, generic parallel processing of large data sets is introduced and its suitability for deployment in the automotive manufacturing industry is considered.

PARALLEL PROCESSING

In general, the most effective parallel processing scheme will depend on the architecture of the host system. The two most common host architectures employed in distributed computing are illustrated in figure 1.

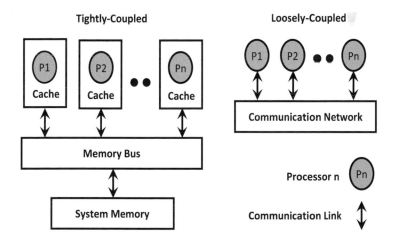

FIGURE 1: Tightly and loosely-coupled architectures. Data is fetched either from the main memory system, via a memory bus, or is transferred over a communications network.

As previously discussed, due to the use of a shared system memory, tightly-coupled architectures allow efficient processing by avoiding data replication and the transfer of information between components. The high cost of hardware required to scale tightly-coupled architectures is however a major disadvantage. It is unlikely, for example, that the hardware employed in a tightly-coupled architecture can be recycled as independent processing units upon retirement. Loosely-coupled architectures, in contrast, have the advantage that the components of a distributed application can reside on existing hardware (Rauber & Runger 2013). This means that an application can be deployed across an existing network making it robust and allowing components to fail without bringing down the entire application. Loosely-coupled architectures have the disadvantage that each component requires communication and collaboration capabilities which allow them to run as separate processes. Unsurprisingly, such capabilities represent overheads which reduce the performance of an application especially when the data to be processed needs to be broken into a large number of segments.

DATA DISTRIBUTION

In tightly-coupled architectures, data distribution is achieved through the installation of a network file systems such as NFS (Sandberg *et al* 1985). A network file system allows all processes to read from and write data to the same address space thus removing the need to physically distribute data across a physical network. Loosely-coupled architecture in contrast require mechanisms to assign data to an area of global memory, the global memory itself being divided into uniquely accessible local partitions to prevent data corruption caused by concurrent reading and writing by multiple processes. System wide data is then added to a global parameters partition, including the number of segments the data is to be divided into and the size of border assigned to each segment, to control the behaviour of the distributed algorithm. Parameters associated with data processing operators, such as local neighbourhood size, are also added to the global partition at this time (Zavorin & Le Moigne 2005). Placing each data segment into a separate partition helps ensure that no single partition becomes excessively large, thus causing a performance bottleneck. The addition of initial system parameters and segment data to their respective partitions is illustrated in figure 2.

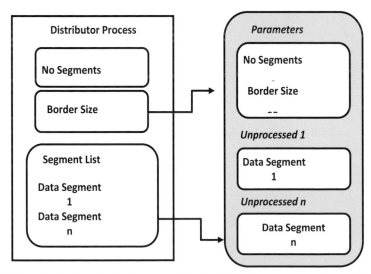

FIGURE 2: Schematic showing a distribution process allocating data and parameters to unique partitions in an area of globally shared memory

LOCAL PROCESSING

Local processing is performed locally by processes residing on a host computer or computers. In a tightly-coupled architecture care must be taken to prevent data corruption caused by concurrent reading and writing by multiple processes on the same data, this is in contrast with loosely-coupled architectures where mutually exclusive access is controlled by the initial partitioning of data segments during the distribution phase. Traditionally, mutually exclusive access to data was implemented as semaphores which act as traffic signals warning processes of the availability of data. More recently this role is shifting to the Integrated Development Environment (IDE), the MathWorks® Distributed Processing Toolbox™ and IDE (MathWorks® 2016) being a prime example of this, which are now capable of warning a programmer when a possible data corruption scenario exists.

In loosely-coupled architectures, parameters associated with the data to be processed are retrieved from the parameters' partition, the local process then waits for a start command. The start command acts as a trigger mechanism which prevents the processes from retrieving data segments before they have been placed in global memory. Once triggered, the data segment associated with a local process is retrieved. The retrieved segment is then processed and placed in a processed partition in the global memory. To reduce search overheads caused by redundant data, whenever a data segment is retrieved from global memory it is removed. The fetch, process and replace cycle is repeated until all data segments have been processed. In a final step, a stop command is sent to all local processes causing them to terminate. Figure 3 illustrates retrieval of operator parameters and data segments by a local process.

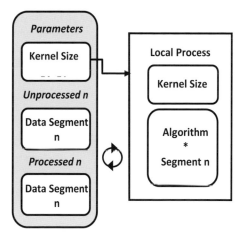

FIGURE 3: Schematic showing the iterative fetch, process and replace cycle of a local process as it repeatedly consumes data segments

DATA ACCUMULATION

In loosely-coupled architectures the accumulation process is similar in implementation terms to the distribution process, the only difference being that it works in reverse order. First, processed data segments are collected from their respective partitions and combined into a single data set. Importantly, the inconsistencies, caused by a lack of a neighbourhood at a data segment's boundary, are eradicated when borders are removed during construction of the resulting data set as described by Grama and colleagues (Grama *et al* 2003). System wide data allocated to the global parameters partition is then removed so as not to influence the behaviour of subsequent distributed algorithms. In tightly-coupled architectures similar housekeeping tasks are also undertaken to enforce data integrity on the system as a whole.

POTENTIAL SOURCES OF BIG DATA

Not only are the automotive production lines generating useful big data, most newly built cars already contain substantial technology coupled to numerous sensors that help improve our driving experience. Detecting if a seat belt is not fastened, automatically switching on headlight or windscreen wipers as well as sensing air pressure in tyres are some simple examples where the potential data generated is huge. In the current technological climate, most of these types of data are stored and processed locally with limited on-board processing capabilities. With the advent of connected cars, it will be possible to aggregate this information into much larger data sets where parallel processing will be employed in the construction of accurate models allowing predictions to be made. The models themselves are also a commodity which could be sold to other manufacturers to improve their product.

Connection to the internet will allow manufacturers to update their vehicle management software remotely, this in turn will allow them to monitor multiple performance metrics and address maintenance issues before they become critical. If, for example, a vehicle is running low on engine oil or the tread on tyres is dangerously low a local garage can be informed with precise details relating to the problem. The car can then be remotely booked in for servicing while the correct components are sent to the garage. By gathering multiple streams of data, parallel processing allows timely inference to be made regarding driver behaviour. For example, establishing if there is a link between how fast people drive and the current weather conditions has the potential to impact car insurance premium rates. These types of big data and ability to mine the insights contained within them are not only useful to the manufacturer themselves but also invaluable commercially to other industries in both their raw and processed forms.

SUITABILITY FOR THE AUTOMOTIVE INDUSTRY

In distributed computing, there are three main modes of operation including fine-grained, coarse-grained and embarrassingly parallel. The inherent parallelism of algorithms is well understood and have been reported by a number of researchers (Rohlfing & Maurer 2003) and (Ino *et al* 2005). Fine-grain parallelism is used to divide an algorithm into low-level components each of which is hosted by a separate processor. Although good for maximising speedup, fine-grain parallelism complicates the distribution of an algorithm and reduces flexibility of the approach; this is mainly because the inter-process communication required for the algorithm to work is high. Coarse-grained parallelism, in contrast, is where inter-process communication is not as frequent but still need to be maintained. Little or no inter-process communication is required in embarrassingly parallel modes of operation. Although entirely plausible, as with other fields of research big data collected from any aspect of the automotive industry will fall into all three categories and expert knowledge will be required to advise on the suitability of a parallel processing scheme and help with the creation of pipelines through which the data can pass.

CONCLUSIONS

This paper is aimed at providing an introduction to the use of parallel processing in the automotive manufacturing industry. Furthermore, the generic parallel processing of large data sets is outlined and its suitability for deployment is considered. From the manufacturers' point of view, the ability to utilise existing hardware makes loosely-coupled architectures attractive to those who already possess extensive computer networks. While those wishing to simplify the processing of their big data will be required to purchase shared memory architectures and associated network infrastructure. To gain competitive advantage manufacturers need to understand customer behaviours in a timely fashion allowing them to make predictions about market trends in advance. Parallel processing of big data is a practical and realistic approach to realising this goal.

References

Eastwood, G. (2017) How Big Data is Transforming the Automotive Industry, Network World, https://www.networkworld.com/article/3200114/big-data/how-big-data-is-transforming-the automotive-industry.html

Englander, I. (2009) The Architecture of Computer Hardware and System Software. An information Technology Approach (4th Ed.), Wiley, ISBN 978-0471715429.

Grama, A. Karypis, G. Kumar, V. and Gupta, A. (2003) Introduction to Parallel Computing: Design and Analysis of Algorithms, Addison Wesley, USA.

Ino, F. Ooyama, K. and Hagihara, K. (2005) A Data Distributed Parallel Algorithm for Non-rigid Image Registration, Parallel Computing, 2005, 31, 19-43.

Lorica, B. (2017) How Big Data and AI will Reshape the Automotive Industry, The O'Reilly Data Show Podcast, https://www.oreilly.com/ideas/how-big-data-and-ai-will-reshape-the-automotive-industry

MathWorks®, (2016). MATLAB Distributed Computing Server ToolboxTM: User's Guide (R2012a). https://www.mathworks.com/help/distcomp/

Nicolescu, C. & Jonker, P. (2000) Parallel Low-level Image Processing on a Distributed Memory System, Proceedings of the 15th Workshop on Parallel and Distributed Processing, pp 226-233.

Rauber, T. & Runger, G. (2013) Parallel Programming: for Multicore and Cluster Systems, Springer Science and Business Media, ISBN 9783642378010.

Rohlfing, T. & Maurer, C.R. (2003) Non-rigid Image Registration in Shared-memory Multi-processor Environments, IEEE Transactions on Information Technology in Biomedicine, 7, 16-25.

Seinstra, F.J. Koelma, D. and Geusebroek, J.M. (2002) A Software Architecture for User Transparent Parallel Image Processing, Parallel Computing, vol. 28, pp. 967-993, 2002.

Sandberg, R. Goldberg, D. Kleiman, S. Walsh, D. and Lydon, B. (1985) Design and Implementation of the Sun Network Filesystem, USENIX.

Zavorin, I. & Le Moigne, J. (2005) Use of Multi-resolution Wavelet Feature Pyramids for Automatic Registration of Multi-sensor Imagery, IEEE Transactions on Image Processing, 2005, 770-782.

Application of Association Rule Mining Technique in Industry 4.0 Process

Mariam Adedoyin-Olowe and Mohamed Medhat Gaber
School of Computing & Digital Technology, Birmingham City University,
Millennium Point, Birmingham, UK. B4 7AP.
Email: {Mariam.adedoyin-olowe, Mohamed.gaber}@bcu.ac.uk

Abstract
Industry 4.0, in all its cutting-edge digitalisation and web technologies in the area of smart machines and products, brings with it the collection and generation of big data that needs to be 'smartly' analysed to aid management and production decision-making process. The application of Association Rule Mining offers Industry 4.0 the affordability to discover and present the co-occurrence of related Association Rules present in Industry 4.0 datasets. In this chapter, we introduce an Architectural Framework built from Association Rule Mining; named Transaction-based Rule Change Mining. The framework is capable of detecting temporal rule dynamics and evolvement of rules in a transactional database of production equipment which can enhance predictive maintenance scheduling.

Keywords
Association Rule Mining, *TRCM*, Industry 4.0

INTRODUCTION

Since the beginning of industrialisation, technological surges have resulted in complete changes which are referred to as *industrial revolutions*. The area of mechanisation resulted in the 1st industrial revolution; the exhaustive use of electrical energy resulted in the 2nd industrial revolution and subsequently, extensive digitalisation resulted in the 3rd industrial revolution (Lasi et al., 2014). The cutting-edge digitalisation in industries, as well as the web technologies and futuristic technologies in the area of smart machines and products, has resulted in a new paradigm shift called *Industry 4.0* – the 4th industrial revolution. In recent times, Industry 4.0 – also referred to as smart manufacturing, smart production and industrial internet etc. (Oesterreich & Teuteberg, 2016) - is attracting accelerated interest from researchers, manufacturers, government and application developers as it enhances energy consumption reduction, economic advantages and smart inventions (Li et al., 2017). The Industry 4.0 has significantly increased the use of ICT in the manufacturing sphere. The increase has encouraged funding programmes and research inventiveness from governments of numerous countries in order to advance or sustain universal relevance in manufacturing production. Industry 4.0 includes diverse technologies that assist the growth of digital and computerised manufacturing settings and also for the digitisation of the value chain.

As industry and society have evolved progressively, the notion of Industry 4.0, smart factories (Liu et al., 2014), networking manufacturing (Davis et al., 2012) and other similar structures have been recommended (Wu et al., 2011; Zhang et al., 2012). Recently, novel information and communication technologies like the industrial cloud (Wan et al., 2014), wireless cloud network (Wan et al., 2013), high performance embedded systems (Wan et al., 2010), industrial internet of things (Chen et al., 2015), big data (Chen et al., 2014; Yin et al., 2015), are now being used in the manufacturing processes to take care of the demand for high productivity and green production. Machines used in manufacturing in Industry 4.0 factories are required to have the abilities of self-cognizance, self-prediction, self-assessment, self-reconfiguration, and self-maintenance (Lee et al., 2014). The predictive maintenance data generated from these

51

machines can be analysed to enhance the regular maintenance scheduling process. However, automated maintenance data collected by factories in Industry 4.0 aggregates into big data and appropriate analytics of such data becomes relevant in order to sustain enhanced performance and the lifespan of the machines.

With the foregoing, application of **Data Mining** techniques to the big data generated from Industry 4.0 production processes can aid predictive maintenance and more importantly, help in unexpected fault detection. This can consequently result in smooth manufacturing processes and performance of industrial machines and better-quality delivery. This chapter presents Transaction-based Rule Change Mining (*TRCM*), an architectural framework developed from Apriori of Association Rule Mining. The *TRCM* architectural framework is capable of detecting temporal rule dynamics and evolvement of rules in a transactional database in the Industry 4.0 production process. For instance, data generated from machines during a production process can be analysed and evaluated using the *TRCM* approach to detect the change in the pattern of scheduled predictive maintenance at two consecutive periods. Application of *TRCM* can rapidly detect faults that may affect productions process in the near future.

OVERVIEW ASSOCIATION RULE MINING

Association Rule Mining (*ARM*) is one of the commonly used data mining techniques. The technique is used for mining significant association rules common to different collections of items in data repositories such as transactional and relational databases (Agrawal *et al.*, 1993, Liu *et al*, 2009). The technique is in form of $X \rightarrow Y$; where X and Y are disjointed sets of items. *ARM* extracts interesting recurrent representation, associations or links between different arrays of items within transactional databases (market basket), relational databases (personal details), or any other information repositories in the form of rules. *ARM* also reveals remarkable associations embedded in huge data sets – such as data sets generated in industry 4.0 – which may include hidden information that can be useful for decision making (Jain et al., 2012). The technique tends to reveal every probable association that satisfies definite boundaries using the defined minimum support and confidence (Ale and Ross, 2000). The *ARM* is mostly used for Market Basket Analysis (*MBA*) to detect the frequency of specific items within the dataset. It evaluates the frequent antecedent/consequent patterns by using support and confidence measures to detect significant relationships (Brin et al., 1997b) that satisfy the user-defined support and confidence thresholds. For instance, *ARM* enables business organisations and industries to understand their customer purchasing behaviour. It is used to ascertain items that are purchased together, for example, bread; milk $\rightarrow$ eggs. This means that customers who buy bread and milk also buys eggs.

$$Rule: \ X \Rightarrow Y$$

$$Support = \frac{frq(X,Y)}{N}$$

$$Confidence = \frac{frq(X,Y)}{frq(X)}$$

$$Lift = \frac{Support}{Supp(X) \times Supp(Y)}$$

FIGURE 1: Association Rule Mining Concepts

ARM enables stores to discover which items sell faster together and those that are not frequently sold. This analysis assists the business when making important business decisions. Items purchased together can be placed within close proximity and those that sell less frequently can be put on offer to attract increased sales.

The rule form of the *ARM* can be demonstrated as follows:

Antecedent → Consequent(user-defined) [support, confidence]

Examples:

Buys (y, "dress") → buys (y, "shoes") [0:5%:60%]

Gender (y, "female") ^ income (y; "50000-55000") → buys (y, "house") [1%; 75%]

However, extracting associations rules from large datasets such as data collected/generated in the Industry 4.0 oftentimes bring about a large amount of discovered rules which end up almost impossible to analyse. Manually inspecting quality rules embedded in these huge datasets is always very tasking and time-consuming.

Support Measures in Association Rule Mining

Support (*S*) of an itemset *I* is the proportion of transactions in the database that is matched by *I* (Bayardo Jr and Agrawal, 1999). This means that an itemset *I* matches a transaction *T* which is part of the whole itemset, where *S* is a subset of *T* (Stahl, 2013, Hipp et al., 2000). The frequency with which the items in I occur collectively in the database is considered. Where support(*S*) = count(*S*)/*n*, given n is the number of transactions in the database. The rule $X \rightarrow Y$ supports if the % support of transactions in T contains $X \cup Y$. Support can also mean a fractional support which means the proportion of transactions that support *X* in *T*. Support can be summarised as follows: Let $K = \{k1; k2; k3..., kn\}$ be a set of items, let *D* (the database), be a set of transactions *T* with each transaction representing the set of items [Srikant and Agrawal, 1996]. T is said to support an item *x* if *x* occurs in *T*, while *T* supports a subset of items *X*. $X \rightarrow Y$ holds if support s is s% of the transactions in *D* that supports *X* also support *Y*. This implies that *T* supports a subset of items *X*. Rules that have support equal to or greater than a user-defined support is said to satisfy the minimum support. Apriori algorithm allows for multiple setting of minimum support threshold without affecting the process of frequent items and rules extraction. Support can be calculated using equation 1.

Confidence Measures in Association Rule Mining

The rule $X \rightarrow Y$ suffice with confidence *(c)* of c% of the transactions that includes *X* also includes *Y* [Agrawal et al., 1993]. Confidence is used to create rules from the frequent itemsets by extracting only rules with c equal to or greater than the user-defined minimum confidence (*min_conf*) .

Lift in Association Rule Mining

The major concern of support and confidence is that of establishing a valid means of deciding the suitable values for *min_sup* and *min_conf*. Setting *min_sup* that is too high will result in missing important rules while setting it too low will generate too many rules, some of which might be irrelevant (Liu et al., 1999). Some rules having uncommon itemsets might be of interest in some situations but the concept of correlation is not being captured. A rule $A \rightarrow B$ that satisfies both the *min_sup* and *min_conf* constraint may not have any correlation between *A* and *B*, which means that support (*A*) × support (*B*) = support (*A* ∪ *B*). Lift chooses rules that have a high score of importance and interestingness (Geng and Hamilton, 2006). It denotes the relation and the difference between the support and if the support would have occurred if *A* and *B* are autonomous. It tends to detect rules with strong correlations between A and B.

THE APRIORI APPROACH TO ASSOCIATION RULE MINING

Apriori method is a common algorithm for learning *ARs* for Boolean associations (Srikant & Agrawal, 1997, Joshi and Sodhi, 2014). Based on prior knowledge of frequent itemset properties, Apriori uses an iterative method named level-wise search to detect frequent itemsets and strong *ARs* (Han & Kamber, 2011). This is achieved by generating a set of all probable combination of items and subsequently computing the support for the itemsets. The downward closure property of frequent patterns (*k-itemset*) implies that any subset of a frequent itemset must be frequent (Zaki & Hsiao, 2002) (*k-1*) as described as follows:

• If a transaction containing {Shoe, bag, belt} is also containing {Shoe, belt}; {Shoe, bag}; {bag, belt}

• {Shoe; bag; belt} is frequent → {Shoe; belt} MUST also be frequent. Any superset of an infrequent itemset are also infrequent and are eradicated from the rule generation.

THE ALGORITHM COMPONENTS OF APRIORI

Since the purpose of data mining techniques (including Apriori) is to solve a specific task, it is imperative to define identified components of the technique. We based our explanations on the work of (Hand et al., 2001) and the components include:

1.   The use of appropriate technique to interpret/address the task; whether classification, clustering, regression or visualisation.

2.   Verification of the model structure adapted to fit the data. The structure encompasses the margins within which learning is affected.

3.   The Score Function (SF) used to evaluate the quality of the fitted models based on the observed data (for example, classification error). The SF can either be maximized or minimized when parameters are fitted to the models/patterns. The SF is vital for learning and generalisation of the models. For Apriori, the SF used is accuracy. For the *ARM*, a method like Apriori rule with favourable interestingness measures can be used as a score function.

4.   The search and optimization method is applied to search the parameters and structures such as computational processes and algorithms used to identify the maximum/minimum of the score function for specific models/ patterns. The concerns arising from this identification include the computational methods employed to enhance the *SF*, for example, search related parameters such as the maximum number of iterations or convergence depiction for an iterative algorithm. For a pattern of a single fixed system such as the kth order polynomial function of the data, the search is carried out in the parameter space to enhance the *SF* comparative to the fixed structural form. In *ARs*, the search is done in accordance with the employed technique, for example, Apriori applies greedy search to find frequent itemsets.

5.   The Data Management Technique employed for storing, indexing and mining data. Accessing large datasets from secondary storage may affect the efficiency of the algorithms, therefore the location of the data and the methods of accessing it are vital.

TRANSACTION-BASED RULE CHANGE MINING – AN APPROACH TO RULE DETECTION IN INDUSTRY 4.0 DATA

Transaction-based Rule Change Mining (*TRCM*) apply Apriori to an interesting keyword in a transactional database within two consecutive periods of time *t* and *t + 1* to produce two association rulesets which are interpreted as rules evolvement in the context of this chapter.

TRCM is a system built to identify rule change patterns in large transaction datasets such as Industry 4.0 data at a different period of time. The application of the Apriori method of an *ARM* to targeted keywords in the document at *t* and *t + 1* generates two association rulesets. In (Adedoyin- Olowe et al., 2013) *TRCM* was used to detect four (temporal) dynamic rules in tweets by emphasising tweet hashtags. The hashtag keywords highlight important words/phrases used in such tweets. The four rules identified are namely **"new rules"**, **"unexpected rules"**, **"emerging rules"** and **"dead rules"**. The rules were obtained by matching rules present in datasets at *t* and *t + 1*. The Rule Matching Threshold (*RMT*) are represented with binary vectors [0; 1], with 0 indicating the non-existence of Association Rules (*ARs*), while 1 indicates the existence of *ARs* in the two datasets. The degree of similarity and difference measures are applied to detect rule changes in the two datasets. The changes are categorised accordingly under the four identified rules. *TRCM* reveals the dynamics of ARs present in transactional databases and demonstrates the linkage between the different types of rule dynamics investigated. The rules at *t* and *t + 1* are matched using **Rule Matching** (*RM*). *RM* is the process of matching the right-hand side/consequent and the left-hand side conditional part of the *ARs* in itemsets at time *t* and *t + 1* to detect keywords at *t + 1* that has any similarity with those at t having considered the user-defined *RMT*. The adoption of *RM* to the two itemsets result in the detection of the four identified rules patterns present in the two datasets. The Architectural Framework of *TRCM* is presented in Figure 2.

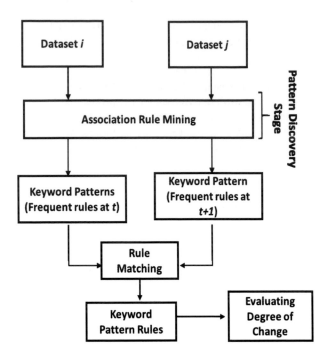

FIGURE 2: TRCM Architectural Framework

Definitions of *TRCM* Rules

Rule Matching in rulesets at t and t+1 results in the definition of *TRCM* rule change patterns. An unexpected Consequent rule arises when a rule at t and another rule at $t + 1$ have a similar conditional part but a different consequent part. An unexpected Conditional rule is detected when the consequent parts of the rule at t and at $t + 1$ are similar, but the conditional parts are different. The similarity measure must be greater than or equal to the user-defined *RMT*. Having described unexpected consequent rule change in the real-life situation, it is important to mention that both unexpected consequent and unexpected conditional rule change are presented in the same way in real life. Unexpected rule evolvement in real life can be likened to the detection of an unexpected fault occurring during the production process. Emerging rules occur when rules at time t and $t + 1$ have similar conditional and consequent parts of the rule with similarity greater than the user-defined threshold.

All rules at $t + 1$ that were not classified as one of the three previous types of rules (emerging, unexpected consequent and unexpected conditional rules) are classified as new rules. This means that all rules in ruleset at $t + 1$ are new until there is a match found in ruleset at t. A rule in t is classified dead if its maximum similarity measure with all the rules in $t + 1$ is less than the user-defined *RMT* from both the conditional and consequent parts. Dead rules in real-life can be a mechanical fault that no longer exists, as a result of permanent eradication of the cause of the fault from re-occurring.

Trend Analysis of Identified Rules

Experimental investigations conducted in (Adedoyin-Olowe et al., 2013, Gomes et al., 2013) show that *ARs* present in datasets at t and $t + 1$ evolve over time. This resulted in what is referred to as rule trend. Trend Analysis (*TA*) in the context of *TRCM* Architecture, is a way of analysing the trend (evolvements) of *TRCM* rules identified in datasets at *t* and *t +1* as displayed by targeted keywords over a specified period of time. The process of TA provides the ability to trace back the root of *TRCM* rules as they evolve from datasets at t and t +1. This process is called rule trace. In the case of a dataset where *faultA* was detected as an unexpected rule - *faultA → ChainJam*) the rule may be traced back to *faultA → SlowChainMovement*. The time frame between these two rule evolvements may vary depending on the period the machine could engage in self-cognizance, self-assessment, self-prediction, self-reconfiguration, and self-maintenance. The evolvements might have been characterised by different occurrences such as the timely intervention of the Operation Manager in attending to the fault.

Application of *TRCM* in Industry 4.0
As mentioned earlier in this chapter, *ARM* extracts interesting recurrent representation, associations or links between different arrays of items within transactional databases (market basket), relational databases (personal details), or any other information repositories in the form of rules. On the other hand, Industry 4.0 is involved in various technologies that promote the growth of digital and computerised manufacturing settings and digitisation of the value chain. In manufacturing, users are interested in wide-ranging maintenance service of production machines through convenient scheduling of corrective maintenance to prevent unexpected machine failures at critical stages of manufacturing procedures. Predictive maintenance of machines ensures optimal performance of the machines as well as improved machines lifespan. In today's technology, machines in Industry 4.0 are maintained using the predictive maintenance technology rather than preventive maintenance procedures commonly used. Predictive maintenance can be applied through sensing, predictive analytics, distributed systems technologies and condition monitoring (Ferreiro et al., 2016).

In a mechanical system, self-awareness refers to the ability to evaluate the present or past state of a machine, and then respond to the valuation output. This can be realised by applying a data-driven algorithm to investigate data collected from the specified machine as well as its location (Lee et al., 2014).

TRCM architecture is an intelligent algorithm, that can be integrated with machines, that has the capacity of performing sensing and predictive analytics to detect Association Rules present in keywords relating to any fault captured in the data. *TRCM* was successfully applied to tweets relating to sports, politics, social-economic and business data (Adedoyin-Olowe et al., 2014, 2015, 2016) to detect evolving Association Rules in tweet hashtags at consecutive periods of time. The detections were correctly mapped to targeted real life events. *TRCM* can be applied to production machines to assist in effective predictive maintenance and track Association Rule Trends of machine performance over a consecutive period of time. This will consequently enhance production management and industry transformation in the long run. *TRCM* rules discovery can be visualised by applying visualisation tools capable of visualising big data output for ease of translation of result outputs for a smooth decision-making process.

CONCLUSIONS

The continuous advancement of smart factories as a result of evolvement of complex production processes in Industry 4.0 has consistently increase the need for the utilisation of advanced prediction models for efficient predictive maintenance scheduling of manufacturing equipment. This has also increased the need for intelligent algorithms to intertwine with smart manufacturing equipment in order to extract and analyse data generated for effective predictive maintenance scheduling of the equipment.

The application of the *TRCM* architectural framework to Industry 4.0 production equipment can help to detect faults by way of detecting change in *ARs* patterns in related datasets. This can improve smart decision support systems for dedicated maintenance scheduling which can consequently enhance manufacturing processes. Application of *TRCM* on manufacturing equipment data can lower maintenance cost and promote the performance and lifespan of equipment, causing an increase in profit and promoting the sustainability of Industry 4.0.

References

Adedoyin-Olowe, M., Gaber, M. M., Dancausa, C. M., Stahl, F., & Gomes, J. B. (2016). A rule dynamics approach to event detection in twitter with its application to sports and politics. Expert Systems with Applications, 55, 351-360.

Adedoyin-Olowe, M., Gaber, M. M., Stahl, F., & Gomes, J. B. (2015). Autonomic discovery of news evolvement in twitter. In Big data in complex systems (pp. 205-229). Springer, Cham.

Adedoyin-Olowe, M., Gaber, M. M., Dancausa, C. M., & Stahl, F. (2014, December). Extraction of unexpected rules from twitter hashtags and its application to sport events. In Machine Learning and Applications (ICMLA), 2014 13th International Conference on (pp. 207-212). IEEE.

Adedoyin-Olowe, M., Gaber, M. M., and Stahl, F. (2013). TRCM: A methodology for temporal analysis of evolving concepts in twitter. In Artificial Intelligence and Soft Computing, pages 135-145. Springer.

Agrawal, R., Imielinski, T., and Swami, A. (1993). Mining association rules between sets of items in large databases. In ACM SIGMOD Record, volume 22, pages 207_216. ACM.

Ale, J. M., & Rossi, G. H. (2000, March). An approach to discovering temporal association rules. In Proceedings of the 2000 ACM Symposium on Applied computing-Volume 1 (pp. 294-300). ACM.

Bayardo Jr, R. J., & Agrawal, R. (1999, August). Mining the most interesting rules. In Proceedings of the fifth ACM SIGKDD international conference on Knowledge discovery and data mining (pp. 145-154). ACM.

Stahl, F., Gaber, M. M., & Bramer, M. (2013). Scaling up data mining techniques to large datasets using parallel and distributed processing. In Business Intelligence and Performance Management (pp. 243-259). Springer, London.

Brettel, M., Friederichsen, N., Keller, M., & Rosenberg, M. (2014). How virtualization, decentralization and network building change the manufacturing landscape: An Industry 4.0 Perspective. International Journal of Mechanical, Industrial Science and Engineering, 8(1), 37-44.

Brin, S., Motwani, R., Ullman, J. D., & Tsur, S. (1997). Dynamic itemset counting and implication rules for market basket data. Acm Sigmod Record, 26(2), 255-264.

Chen, M., Mao, S., & Liu, Y. (2014). Big data: A survey. Mobile Networks and Applications, 19(2), 171–209.

Davis, J., Edgar, T., Porter, J., Bernaden, J., & Sarli, M. (2012). Smart manufacturing, manufacturing intelligence and demand-dynamic performance. Computers and Chemical Engineering, 47, 145–156.

Ferreiro, S., Konde, E., Fernández, S., & Prado, A. (2016, June). Industry 4.0: Predictive Intelligent Maintenance for Production Equipment. In European Conference of the Prognostics and Health Management Society, no (pp. 1-8).

GENG, L. and HAMILTON, H. J. (2006). Interestingness measures for data mining: A survey. ACM Computing Surveys (CSUR), 38(3), 9.

Gomes, J. B., Adedoyin-Olowe, M., Gaber, M. M., & Stahl, F. (2013). Rule type identification using trcm for trend analysis in twitter. In Research and development in intelligent systems xxx (pp. 273-278). Springer, Cham.

Hipp, J., Güntzer, U., & Nakhaeizadeh, G. (2000). Algorithms for association rule mining—a general survey and comparison. ACM sigkdd explorations newsletter, 2(1), 58-64.

Han, J., Pei, J., & Kamber, M. (2011). Data mining: concepts and techniques. Elsevier.

Joshi, A., & Sodhi, J. S. (2014). Target advertising via association rule mining. International Journal, 2(5), 256-261.

Lasi, H., Fettke, P., Kemper, H. G., Feld, T., & Hoffmann, M. (2014). Industry 4.0. Business & Information Systems Engineering, 6(4), 239-242.

Lee, J., Kao, H. A., & Yang, S. (2014). Service innovation and smart analytics for industry 4.0 and big data environment. Procedia Cirp, 16, 3-8.

Li, X., Li, D., Wan, J., Vasilakos, A. V., Lai, C. F., & Wang, S. (2017). A review of industrial wireless networks in the context of industry 4.0. Wireless networks, 23(1), 23-41.

Liu, Q., Wan, J., & Zhou, K. (2014). Cloud manufacturing service system for industrial-cluster-oriented application. Journal of Internet Technology, 15(3), 373–380.

Liu, B., Hsu, W., & Ma, Y. (1999, August). Mining association rules with multiple minimum supports. In Proceedings of the fifth ACM SIGKDD international conference on Knowledge discovery and data mining (pp. 337-341). ACM.

Oesterreich, T. D., & Teuteberg, F. (2016). Understanding the implications of digitisation and automation in the context of Industry 4.0: A triangulation approach and elements of a research agenda for the construction industry. Computers in Industry, 83, 121-139.

Srikant, R., Vu, Q., & Agrawal, R. (1997, August). Mining association rules with item constraints. In Kdd (Vol. 97, pp. 67-73).

Srikant, R., & Agrawal, R. (1996, June). Mining quantitative association rules in large relational tables. In Acm Sigmod Record (Vol. 25, No. 2, pp. 1-12). ACM.

Wan, J., Zhang, D., Zhao, S., Yang, L. T., & Lloret, J. (2014). Context-aware vehicular cyber-physical systems with cloud support: Architecture, challenges and solutions. *IEEE Communications Magazine, 52*(8), 106–113.

Wan, J., Zou, C., Ullah, S., Lai, C., Zhou, M., & Wang, X. (2013). Cloud-enabled wireless body area networks for pervasive healthcare. *IEEE Network, 27*(5), 56–61.

Wu, F. J., Kao, Y. F., & Tseng, Y. C. (2011). From wireless sensor networks towards cyber physical systems. *Pervasive and Mobile Computing, 7*(4), 397–413.

Yin Zhang, Y., Qiu, M., Tsai, C. W., Hassan, M. M., & Alamri, A. (2015). Health-CPS: Healthcare cyber-physical system assisted by cloud and big data. *IEEE Systems Journal*. doi: 10.1109/JSYST.2015.2460747.

Zaki, M. J., & Hsiao, C. J. (2002, April). CHARM: An efficient algorithm for closed itemset mining. In Proceedings of the 2002 SIAM international conference on data mining (pp. 457-473). Society for Industrial and Applied Mathematics.

Zhang, Y., Zhang, D., Hassan, M. M., Alamri, A., & Peng, L. (2015). CADRE: Cloud-assisted drug recommendation service for online phARMacies. *Mobile Networks and Applications, 20*(3), 348–355.

Zhang, D., Wan, J., Liu, Q., Guan, X., & Liang, X. (2012). A Taxonomy of agent technologies for ubiquitous computing environments. *KSII Transactions on Internet and Information Systems, 6*(2), 547–565.

Challenges in Cybersecurity for Industry 4.0

Vitor Jesus and Mark Josephs

School of Computing and Digital Technology
Birmingham City University
City Centre Campus, Millennium Point, Birmingham, UK. B4 7XG.
Email: {vitor.jesus,Mark.Josephs}@bcu.ac.uk

Abstract

Industry 4.0 is an ongoing transformation that aligns Industry with new computing and business models. Examples of enabling technologies are Cloud Computing, Cyber-Physical Systems, Artificial Intelligence and Big Data. Some technologies are well established in other sectors, such as Financial and IT, but the adaptation effort is nevertheless significant. Among the risks, cybersecurity is at the forefront. This chapter discusses why Industry 4.0 brings unprecedented cybersecurity challenges to Manufacturing and the overall Industrial sector. To overcome them, we make the case for new codes of practice that take a holistic view of the IT and OT world whilst adopting a framework that should be native to Industry 4.0.

Keywords

Cybersecurity, Industry 4.0, Industrial Internet

INTRODUCTION

Industry 4.0 (or "Industrie 4.0" as the German initiative is called) is now on the agenda of all industrial sectors as the Fourth Industrial Revolution. Similar initiatives, although with important differences, exist elsewhere with the Industrial Internet (from the United States) being at the forefront. Given that there are more similarities than differences, we shall collectively refer to these initiatives as Industry 4.0 (I4.0). In our opinion, I4.0 is more likely to be an evolution than a revolution but one that, nevertheless, will transform industry and manufacturing. A 2014 report from PricewaterhouseCoopers envisioned €140 billion annual spending by European industry until 2020 with more than 80% of companies seeing their value chain digitised and an increase of productivity of 18% (PricewaterhouseCoopers, 2014).

The notion of digitisation is central to I4.0. In opposition to Information Technologies[1] (IT), that essentially handle information, materials cannot be digitised. However, the operations environment concerning People, Processes and Products (commonly called the 3P) can indeed be digitised with the corresponding improvements in productivity (Thames & Schaefer 2016). Furthermore, it enables new business models where different parties, not necessarily connected, collaborate to create new products, sometimes called Social Products (Rüßmann et al 2015), in an agile way. Such digitisation has two main axes: vertically, it should cover the business units of the same organisation, from the plant to the business intelligence; horizontally, it should cover the whole supply chain, from customers to suppliers to partners or agencies

---

[1] In this chapter, we collectively call IT any field that is not Industrial while fully appreciating that other fields, such as Telecommunications or Medical devices, do not perfectly fall under Information Technologies.

I4.0 is, in the first place, a convergence of traditional manufacturing techniques with current trends in information technologies. It goes beyond that, however, as it also sets a new paradigm in terms of business collaboration and the use of technology with two overarching goals, namely, zero-defects and turnaround efficiency from design to finished product.

The opportunity to rethink Industry comes at a time when a number of key technologies has matured sufficiently – such as Cloud Computing and Mobile Technologies – technologies that are ready to be embedded in a sector that is traditionally conservative and/or has long upgrade cycles. Past the effort involved in the transformation, cybersecurity is raised as a top concern of business leaders (Bughin et al 2015), given the exploding complexity of the technologies involved, which creates risks and an attack surface that did not exist before. In a simplistic way, what before could be protected with walls and physical security, now requires a matching level of sophistication and management. The remainder of this chapter is organised as follows. In the next section, we review the key technologies involved in I4.0, and then go on to identify the old and new cybersecurity risks. In the last section, we propose directions for mitigation of the identified risks.

Industry 4.0 enablers

We start by reviewing the key elements of Industry 4.0 to guide the later discussion on cybersecurity. We split the key enablers of Industry 4.0 into four categories: Cyber-Physical Systems (CPS); Cloud-assisted Manufacturing; Mobile Technologies and Augmented Reality; and Big Data, Artificial Intelligence and Analytics.

Cyber-Physical Systems

CPS are any systems that provide an interface between the computing infrastructure and the physical reality. A simple split is sensors and actuators that are enabled with networking interfaces in order to report measurements and/or actuate on the physical environment (Igor 2016). Internet-of-Things is a close concept, although the CPS mostly relate to the physical devices and IoT typically combine devices and a cloud counterpart. Consider a scenario of an automotive wheel made of a light alloy containing magnesium or aluminium with each unit needing to have a unique identifier. A simple example of a CPS is an actuator that marks the wheel with a Quick Response (QR) code and a set of sensors that later track the same code in order for each manufactured unit to have a globally unique identity (Cheng et al 2016).

CPS may also take the form of embedded devices that have computing capabilities and run a complex embedded Operating System, such as Linux or QNX. Depending on the application, such devices may process data before sending to a centralised point (that can be in the Cloud). An alternative is to send the data to other nearby intermediary devices that will pre-process and aggregate data from multiple devices before sending to a central architecture to either control an industrial process or for analysis – a so-called Fog Computing architecture (Peralta et al 2017). Considering that the backbone of Industry 4.0 is the digitisation of the manufacturing process, CPS play a central role as they are expected to be pervasive both vertically, from data at the plant floor to business analytics, and horizontally by communicating reliable data to multiple stakeholders. A key element associated with CPS is, naturally, industrial robots. By achieving increasingly greater autonomy, the human element can be removed from adverse environments with corresponding efficiency and flexibility gains. When fully integrated in the Smart Factory, robots are on the critical path of end-to-end digitisation.

Cloud-assisted Manufacturing

Cloud Computing is a fairly recent, yet mature, paradigm for computing that relies on using shared and remote resources, often in an imprecise physical location or distributed across multiple ones. In terms of business, this model has several advantages when considering the Total Cost of Ownership of a server infrastructure which, beyond economies of scale, has important manageability properties since the physical infrastructure is often outsourced. Cloud computing intensively uses virtualisation techniques that allow a multi-tenancy model: multiple users have access to the same physical server while applications and services run as if using dedicated hardware. A common provider of a (public) Cloud is Amazon with its Amazon Web Services: using simple interfaces, servers and services can be deployed extremely quickly – minutes in contrast with the months it might take to buy and provision an actual server infrastructure before applications and services can be installed.

A common way of defining a cloud paradigm is to say that its adoption converts resources and processes into programmatic software interfaces. An industrial use case would be customer fulfilment that is as simple as placing an order and uploading CAD files on a web site, then waiting for the package to be delivered. The cloud service sets in motion all the required manufacturing processes, internally manages scheduling and availability of resources and hands-over the product to other parties for further handling and delivery. Such on-demand self-service is a possible delivery model and is particularly applicable when considering Additive Manufacturing (AM). Although not commonly used in today's die cast industry, where mostly alternative methods depending on the product are used, AM is commonly considered one of the enablers of Industry 4.0. In AM, manufacturing is often envisioned as evolving to a model where any part with any geometry can be uploaded to be (3D-) printed with high efficiency in raw materials waste.

Cloud-assisted Manufacturing takes advantage of this computing model to enable new business models. Not only does it have the potential of virtualising, via software interfaces, physical processes, but it has also the ability of combining and matching suppliers, providers, tools and space in order to create value (Mabkhot et al 2018) from the composition of virtualised services. In fact, one can imagine a full virtualised factory in this way, where multiple specialised suppliers are composed using an online tool that more or less autonomously organises and defines the workflow, from the design files to physical delivery. Another example is a customer creating different customised products. Such horizontal integration of multiple parties dynamically cooperating along a chain of value is also seen as a key driver towards Smart Factories (Strange 2017).

Mobile Technologies and Augmented Reality

Mobility and Augmented Reality are, in this scope, tightly connected. We gather here those requirements that enable different stakeholders, from a business owner to an operator, to have access anywhere and anytime to required and detailed information, in a human-friendly way, or even be able to control a process remotely. Whereas mobile technologies in conjunction with a Cloud infrastructure, enable an anywhere-anytime-anyone paradigm, Augmented Reality creates new usability patterns. For example, a CAD model can be virtually manipulated in real-time as if it is a physical object and, given availability of information, can even be visually matched with a part during its manufacture.

Big data and Artificial Intelligence

Techniques to analyse large volumes of data, both offline and in real-time, are now available that allow unprecedented efficiency, both in terms of obtaining the current status of a process or workflow and in terms of identifying hidden trends and value. Whereas Big Data is the set of technologies that enable the analysis of very large volumes of information, Artificial Intelligence (AI), in its primary form as Machine Learning, consists of giving inference capabilities to computer systems. The vision is that information is collected at many different points and lifecycles, with collection points ranging from CPS to business workflows (logistics, finance, scheduling, etc.) and sent to be analysed. The data mining can be used at any point in the business: from real-time data to assist the industrial processes to business analytics to inform strategic and operational decisions.

.

The Cybersecurity Challenge

Industry 4.0 dramatically changes the threat landscape in comparison to traditional manufacturing. For one thing, its inherent technological basis dramatically increases the attack surface, exposing a business or process to the possibility of being compromised in many different ways. Furthermore, the human element is now a key source of risks: considering the dense network of actors in the chain of value of I4.0, from users to suppliers, third-parties and inter-domain interfaces now pose a management problem that was much smaller (often negligible) before. We now discuss how Industry 4.0 impacts cybersecurity practices.

Operational Technologies versus Information Technologies

A simple starting model in cybersecurity is the CIA triangle: Confidentiality, Integrity and Availability. Different sectors have different priorities. Whereas a financial business will be mostly concerned with Confidentiality and Integrity, an electricity supplier will focus its security practices on Availability. Manufacturers would typically focus on either Availability, in the case of high-volume but low added-value products, or Integrity, in the opposite case. By Integrity, one means a high-quality, repeatable and accurate production. Industry 4.0 requires all three elements at the same level of attention.

When compared with Information Technologies, securing Operational Technologies (OT) has inherently different requirements – Table 1 briefly makes a comparison. For diverse reasons, OT requires a cybersecurity approach that is distinct from IT and the first author has first-hand experience in seeing cybersecurity programmes designed with IT in mind systematically fail or quickly be found to be inadequate. One reason is to do with the difference of cultures between the two domains. Whereas IT uses widespread and conventional technologies, that get updated and upgraded in very short cycles, OT projects can take years to develop and can have a field longevity of decades. Furthermore, industrial projects always have, regardless of the sector, a safety-critical element. It is often said that, if an IT system fails, the business gets phone calls from angry users, but if a furnace explodes it can take human lives. OT is nevertheless converging with IT, both in terms of adapting mature and advanced IT technologies to OT projects and also because IT is increasingly seeing requirements that once were only for OT – for example, with operations running on a 24x7x365 basis. Another reason is that OT equipment and software is usually different from what is found in IT, coming from different, specialised vendors whose software development processes often do not have the maturity, or the same resources, as those of well-known vendors. The result is that devices are often more limited in terms of features and support is not as agile, which impacts on the cybersecurity world when it comes to vulnerability management and updates.

It is also worth pointing out that cybersecurity for OT has only recently started to be taken seriously throughout the sector. It can be argued that the Stuxnet case (Lachow 2011) in Iran, 2010, was a turning point for industrial cybersecurity. Since then, the world has seen multiple high-profile incidents, while numerous small ones remain to be analysed. Cybersecurity for OT was, until then, often considered a lesser concern. In fact, cybersecurity for OT relied – and still often does – in physical isolation of the plant from the rest of the business, the so-called "air gap". This apparently seems to reduce the problem to one of physical security which has been repeatedly proven to not provide the expected assurances (Cisco Blogs 2018). For example, industrial networks often have wireless access points in order to facilitate remote maintenance, but attackers can exploit them too.

Table 1 – Requirements of OT versus IT

	Information Technologies (IT)	**Operational Technologies (OT)**
Different Industries	Enterprise, Datacentres, Financial, Services	Energy, Oil&Gas, Manufacturing, Automotive, Transportation, Smart Cities, Smart Buildings
Different Goals	Information-centric: data confidentiality, business support, can usually be stopped if necessary; fast development and obsolescence lifecycles (5y)	Process-centric: 24x7x365 availability, critical infrastructure, real-time interactions, cannot usually be stopped (societal/environmental); long project lifecycles (up to 25 years)
Different Technologies & Vendors	Servers, Enterprise networks, Applications, Web, End-user, laptops and mobile devices	PLCs, Remote telemetry, HMIs, historians, industrial or real-time protocols, raw materials, critical real-time control, telemetry centric, field devices, mixed technologies (OS, embedded, proprietary, legacy)
Different Practices	ISO 27001; OWASP; CISSP; EU/GDPR; SOC; FedRAMP; CSA	ISA99/IEC62443; GIAC GICSP; Industry specific; Operations Reliability

Increased Surface Attack of Industry 4.0

Industry 4.0 removes the split between IT and OT while dramatically increasing the surface attack of compared to traditional manufacturing. We identify four main reasons: the inherent complexity of I4.0, assimilation of IT risks, transition and change management, and, finally, Third-Party management.

Scale and Complexity

Industry 4.0 is a system-of systems which raises unparalleled complexity and scale when compared to traditional manufacturing, given the expected dense interconnectivity between processes, products and people. To contrast, whereas before the industrial processes could simply be protected inside a physically secure space, now the myriad of devices and systems can be converted to a point of compromise, which can be remote and from which the whole business becomes vulnerable. Such complexity and scale needs to be properly managed across the lifecycle of a security programme which has both a technical and business dimension. Furthermore, considering all risks, a single successful attack is now able to cause significant damage (in the order of the investment effort in Industry 4.0) if cybersecurity is not designed in from the outset.

A striking source of complexity and scale is the ubiquity of networked CPS that now become an attack vector. For example, a CPS in a I4.0 setting should to be reconfigurable which raises its software complexity and increases the risk of vulnerabilities – in fact, it could conflict with safety requirements. A key risk is a CPS running compromised software which is only fairly addressed by using trusted hardware (cryptographic functions directly implemented on electronics) (Waidner & Kasper 2016) and which is harder to develop software for. Table 2 lists some of the high-level threats to which CPS are exposed. A successful attack rarely uses a single vector; instead, they are usually a combination of actions and steps that may take months to carry out until a goal is reached. A common technique is lateral movements: a device is compromised only to serve as a foothold and, from there, other devices or systems are compromised in accordance with a strategic plan.

Table 2 – some cybersecurity attacks associated with CPS

Attack type	Description
Physical	Changing the hardware or software by physically modifying it.
Impersonation	A malicious device hiding between legitimate devices.
Man-in-the-middle	Intercepting and/or modifying in-flight communications
DoS	Denial of Service: compromise availability of services, machines or communications
Malware	Malicious software installed and undetected

Assimilation of IT risks and requirements

Off the plant floor, the I4.0 factory will bring in all the risks that IT currently has which will add to the typical risks of OT. The Cloud component is an example – see Table 3 for typical attacks. On the one hand, exposing software interfaces to the public Internet will attract remote attacks and will facilitate reconnaissance, a key stage in any attack where discovery of vulnerabilities is made. On the other hand, mobile users will have access to important assets and will have to use trusted devices and, above all, have enough training in order to be aware of the risks and cybersecurity best-practices. The current trend of Bring-Your-Own-Device (BYOD) will require special measures as a trade-off between efficiency, personal freedom and cybersecurity is likely to exist.

Table 3 – some cybersecurity attacks associated with Cloud Computing

Attack type	Description
Data Breaches	Stealing valuable data
Account mismanagement	Compromised credentials or keeping legitimate owners out of service
Insecure interfaces	The software interfaces used in interacting with the cloud are vulnerable
DoS	Denial of Service: compromise availability of services, machines or communications
Compliance violation	Storing or using data in a fashion not compliant with regulations
Compromised shared hardware	The servers on which the applications and services run are compromised.
Man in the middle	Capturing data in transit or tampering with service requests

Revisiting the scenario where a customer uploads to the Cloud a CAD file of a part that needs to be manufactured, the file eventually reaches the plant floor but may be compromised with subtle modifications that could be difficult to detect. A case in die cast or additive manufacturing is adding seemingly imperceptible imperfections, such as indents or voids (Cao et al 2015), which weaken or otherwise lower the quality of the final part. Even worse, new smart file types to be designed (CAD, STL, tooling files) may be prone to embedding executable malware which may be a door to an attacker.

Data quality is also now a requirement. A possible attack on Artificial Intelligence agents is where they are remotely re-trained, using legitimate interactions such as a set of customers feeding inconsistent data, in order to skew their inference processes. Overall, a data quality attack is such that data used is subtly contaminated in order to cause inaccuracies.

Finally, one major challenge is the early state of integrated cybersecurity frameworks for Industry 4.0 (Waidner & Kasper 2016). It should be noted that whereas IT is rich in cybersecurity standards and guidance, some at the regulatory level, OT is not. A sign of this is looking at current I4.0 models such as RAMI or IIRA (Ma et al 2017) and realising, surprisingly, that cybersecurity is something of an afterthought.

Transition Management

It is expected that the transition between traditional and smart factories will take time and several upgrade cycles. This means that traditional and modern devices, systems and processes will coexist. There are two cybersecurity implications. The first is that old vulnerable devices will have less cybersecurity capabilities, or have vulnerabilities that cannot be patched. They will, expectedly also be hard, if not impossible, to retrofit and will integrate in a less ideal way with the I4.0 architecture. This requires mitigations based on perimeter infrastructure such as Intrusion Detection Systems which is challenging on its own for Industry 4.0 (Rubio et al 2017) given the heterogeneity of devices, industries and applications.

Secondly, history has proven that change management creates its own vulnerabilities. There are countless examples of forgotten servers or devices that, in the extreme case, are openly accessible on the Internet. In any project, managing change is always complex, both in terms of resources and realignment with processes; in cybersecurity it can temporarily, yet dramatically, raise risks.

Finally, a note on cybersecurity operations. With scale, threat intelligence and incident monitoring become complex bringing the problem to the levels of large IT infrastructures. Even if engineers have proven skills in complex process monitoring, cybersecurity requires different techniques and technologies which may require significant effort in order to adjust and prepare (Moustafa et al 2018).

Third Party Management and Context

Finally, Industry 4.0 brings a new challenge for Manufacturing that typically did not exist before. Given the dynamic business context composed of many parties, administrative borders become critically important: customers, suppliers and partners are now part of the operations. A comprehensive cybersecurity programme needs to account for the lack of good cybersecurity practices of Third Parties.

It is always challenging, in any industry, to manage the cybersecurity of Third parties since, by definition, a business has only signed agreements at their disposal or, at best, some powers to audit that are always limited. Other than that, a simple sharing of a credential to upload, for example, a design file of a part can compromise the whole business. Old problems, such as auditing the provenance of materials and parts are now scaled up.

Furthermore, Confidentiality and Privacy are now also strong requirements. By opening to the wider business context, Intellectual Property of customers, for example, has to be managed in a structured and consistent way. This further opens the space to Regulations connected to cybersecurity. For example, the recent EU directive Networks and Information Systems (NIS), that is essentially a cybersecurity regulation, mostly applies to critical infrastructure operators but will indirectly affect suppliers and intermediaries.

Finally, considerations must be given to incident response and forensics (Eden et al 2016). In handling an incident, as it may escalate up to involving regulatory authorities, there may be a duty to collect evidence in a legally acceptable way. Whereas components sourced from the IT domain typically have security controls in place, such as audit logs, OT components typically do not. Furthermore, collecting evidence in real-time during production may prove extremely challenging and needs to be avoided at all costs.

Perspectives

The rise in sophistication of Industry 4.0 can only be matched by raising the sophistication of the cybersecurity approach itself. Whereas IT practices are robust and mature in their essence, they cannot fully cover the Industrial case. As such, a mix of practices and technologies, both new and old, needs to be drawn upon in order to design a comprehensive cybersecurity programme for Industry 4.0. Figure 1 (left) gives a representative lifecycle of a cybersecurity programme, typically designed for IT. It should be contrasted with Figure 1 (right) that shows a typical model for Manufacturing. Beyond protecting the human, always the top priority, cybersecurity has to be supported by a business case and it is in this sense that it is currently evolving, from a management perspective, as a risk discipline, similar to other business domains (Radanliev et al 2018). An alternative would be to decompose the overall problem of the Industry 4.0 factory and progressively identify and break down possible risks which are then mitigated using either processes or technologies informed by standards and community guidance. Ultimately, as Figure 1 (right) shows, it is integrated into the business strategy and governance.

Considering the diversity of elements in Industry 4.0 that form a continuum between different areas (for example, CPS to Cloud to Business IT), we argue that a combination of current cybersecurity approaches may not completely close all the gaps; rather, a specific approach to Industry 4.0 may prove to be necessary with selective implementation of relevant codes of practice where applicable.

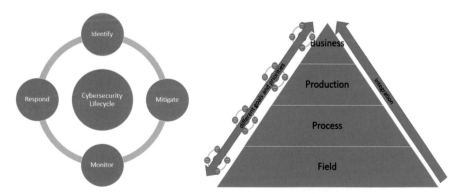

FIGURE 1: Cybersecurity Governance.

A number of standards exist that can be of help. Table 4 lists some of the prevalent standards and guidance in cybersecurity. IEC/ISA 62443 is particularly fit for Industry 4.0. With current adoption mainly in Oil & Gas, it is a flexible framework for Industrial environments. Others, depending on the particular domain of the Smart Factory, should be used. For example, ISO 27001 should be used to manage a cybersecurity programme based on risk, despite being oriented to Information; and CSA STAR on the cloud subdomain.

Table 4 – Cybersecurity related standards and guidance.

Guidance	Domain	Aim
ISO 27001, SOC 2	IT	IT cybersecurity management
CSA STAR, CIS, ISO 27018	IT, Cloud	Security in the cloud
EU/GDPR	IT	Data Privacy regulation (EU)
NIST	Various	Catalogue of recommendations (US)
OWASP, ISO 27034	IT (Web)	Secure software development
IEC/ISA 62443	Industrial	Industrial and SCADA cybersecurity

Finally, one aspect that can be of help is that Industry 4.0 will accelerate the convergence between IT and OT which may have the benefit of standardising OT technologies in the direction of IT and enable the reuse of mature IT cybersecurity technologies in OT. Examples are next-generation firewalls or Intrusion Detection Systems (Rubio 2017) which are commonly less featured in OT than their counterpart in IT.

CONCLUSIONS

This chapter discussed the challenges that Industry 4.0 face regarding cybersecurity. Because of its transformative character and the complexity of system-of-systems, involving several different technical and business visions, multiple challenges were identified. The paradigm still has to mature and materialise in concrete use-cases as the ones available for analysis are still sparse. Furthermore, cybersecurity frameworks for I4.0 are still lacking which includes models to manage the transition and coexistence of traditional and I4.0 domains. A different framework is therefore needed that, on the one hand, is able to integrate the multiple domains that comprise the new Industrial paradigm (which current standards are able to address) but, on the other hand, has to be native to Industry 4.0 given its own emergent properties.

References

Bughin, J., Chui, M. and Manyika, J. (2015), An executive's guide to the internet of things, McKinsey Quarterly, Vol. 4, pp. 92-101, 2015

Cao, B, et al (2015), Research and Practice on Aluminium Industry 4.0, 6th Intl Conf on Intelligent Control and Information Processing, Wihan, China, Nov 2015

Cheng, F-T et al (2016), Industry 4.1 for Wheel Machining Automation, IEEE Robotics and Automation Letters, vol. 1, no. 1, January 2016

Cisco Blogs (2018), HAVEX Proves (Again) that the Airgap is a Myth: Time for Real Cybersecurity in ICS Environments, https://blogs.cisco.com/digital/havex-proves-again-that-the-airgap-is-a-myth-time-for-real-cybersecurity-in-ics-environments, July 3, 2014 (accessed 21 August 2018)

Eden, P, et al (2016), SCADA System Forensic Analysis Within IIoT, Springer Series in Advanced Manufacturing, Cybersecurity for Industry 4.0, 2016

Igor, H, Bohuslava, J, Martin, J (2016), Proposal of communication standardization of industrial networks in Industry 4.0, 20th IEEE Intl Conf on Intelligent Engineering Systems, June 2016, Budapest, Hungary

Lachow, I, (2011), The Stuxnet Enigma: Implications for the Future of Cybersecurity, Georgetown Journal of International Affairs, International Engagement on Cyber: Establishing International Norms and Improved Cybersecurity, 2011, pp. 118-126

Ma, Z, Hudic, A, Shaaban, A, Plosz, S (2017), Security Viewpoint in a Reference Architecture Model for Cyber-Physical Production Systems, IEEE European Symposium on Security and Privacy Workshops (EuroS&PW), 2017

Mabkhot, MM, Al-Ahmari, MA, Salah, B, Alkhalefah, H (2018), Requirements of the Smart Factory System: A Survey and Perspective, Machines, MDPI, v6, i23, June 2018

Moustafa, N, et al (2018), A New Threat Intelligence Scheme for Safeguarding Industry 4.0 Systems, IEEE Access, v6, 2018

Peralta, G, Iglesias-Urkia, M, Barcelo, M, Gomez, R, Moran, A, and Bilbao J (2017), Fog computing based efficient IoT scheme for the Industry 4.0, IEEE International Workshop of Electronics, Control, Measurement, Signals and their Application to Mechatronics (ECMSM), Donostia-San Sebastian, 2017, pp. 1-6

PricewaterhouseCoopers (2014), Industry 4.0 – Opportunities and Challenges of the Industrial Internet, Dec 2014

Radanliev, P, et al (2018), Integration of Cyber Security Frameworks, Models and Approaches for Building Design Principles for the Internet-of-Things in Industry 4.0, Living in the Internet of Things: Cybersecurity of the IoT, London, 2018

Rubio, JE, Roman, R, Lopez J (2017), Analysis of cybersecurity threats in Industry 4.0: the case of intrusion detection, CRITIS 2017

Rüßmann, M, Lorenz, M, Gerbert, P, Waldner, M, Justus, J, Engel, P, and Harnisch, M, (2015), Industry 4.0: The Future of Productivity and Growth in Manufacturing Industries, The Boston Consulting Group, April 2015

Strange, R, Zucchella, A (2017), Industry 4.0, global value chains and international business, Multinational Business Review, Vol. 25, Issue 3

Thames, L, Schaefer, D (2016), Industry 4.0: An Overview of Key Benefits, Technologies, and Challenges, Springer Series in Advanced Manufacturing, Cybersecurity for Industry 4.0, 2016

Waidner, M, and Kasper, M (2016), Security in industrie 4.0 - challenges and solutions for the fourth industrial revolution, Design, Automation & Test in Europe Conference & Exhibition (DATE), Dresden, 2016

Applications of Augmented Reality in Manufacturing

Cham Athwal, Maite Frutos-Pascual and Ian Williams

DMT Lab, School of Computing and Digital Technology, Birmingham City University,
Millennium Point, Birmingham, UK. B4 7XG.
Email: {cham.athwal@bcu.ac.uk, maite.frutos@bcu.ac.uk and ian.williams}@bcu.ac.uk

Abstract

Current advances in Augmented Reality (AR) hardware and software has largely mitigated the key adoption barriers for presenting a practical application of AR. Complimentary to this the recent development of commercial portable AR devices, notably the MS Hololens, now presents a viable platform for changing many key manufacturing practices and therefore redesigning legacy processes. This paper presents the current potential of AR for supporting manufacturing. We firstly introduce general concepts of AR and establish the current positioning of AR research and hardware. We then present several key application domains whereby AR can be readily applied, notably in production assistance, operator navigation, product visualisation and manual training. We finally present some current barriers to AR adoption in manufacturing and highlight the current limitations that should be considered when looking to develop and apply a practical application of AR.

Keywords

Augmented Reality (AR), Virtual Reallity (VR), Manufacturing, Training, Interaction.

INTRODUCTION

Augmented Reality (AR) refers to technology that presents the *real* world to the user but *augmented* with virtual components (usually Computer Generated Images) that appear to be part of the real world. This can be contrasted with Virtual Reality where the user is totally immersed within a virtual world usually with no reference to the user's actual surroundings. These immersive technologies are widely expected to become one of the major enablers of Industry 4.0 and digitisation more generally. Overall global Augmented Reality/ Virtual Reality revenues are set to rocket from £4.2 billion in 2016 to £130 billion in 2020 (International Data Corporation (IDC)), with the United Kingdom (UK) set to be at the epicentre of this market growth, second after the United States in market share (GrowthEnabler Market Pulse Report AR & VR). The Made Smarter Review, led by Professor Juergen Maier, CEO Siemens UK, and commissioned by the UK Government to set out how UK manufacturing can be transformed through the adoption of industrial digital technology (IDT) also identified AR/VR as one of its 5 key enabling technologies. The consensus is that, although currently (2018) VR has greater uptake due to the availability during the past couple of years of consumer accessible VR Head Mounted Displays (HMDs) such as Oculus Rift and HTC Vive, with large audiences for games and entertainment application, the major growth in industrial use will be for AR supported by nascent HMD's and Smart Glasses such as Microsoft's Hololens, Meta 2 and Magic Leap.

Car manufacturers such as BMW and Jaguar Land Rover have recently started to introduce AR experiences into their market strategies, enabling potential customers to customise and take a closer look of their cars using immersive technology. International shipment company DHL has introduced AR into their supply chain logistics, making smart glasses the new standard in their warehouses and showcasing improvements in productivity, according to their press release.

71

WHAT IS AR?

AR is a set of technologies that seeks to give their user the impression that virtual (computer generated) objects are actually present in the same space as the real world surrounding them. The virtual objects are most often 3D models existing within a computer defined co-ordinate reference frame that have to be rendered onto a display by the AR system. Although, numerous display formats (including holographic and volumetric projection systems) have been postulated and prototyped, current commercially available AR systems largely present the virtual objects on a screen in either video see through (VST) or optical see through (OST) modes. Tablets, smartphones and head mounted devices are typically used for VST based AR; the virtual objects are rendered and composited onto the video stream captured by the camera or cameras on these devices. OST based AR currently is available on HMD's and Smart Glasses; in this case the virtual objects are presented on the surface of a semi-transparent screen through which the user can see the real world directly.

In AR applications the illusion that the virtual object is actually in the real world is maintained because the virtual object's rendering will change with head movement in the same way as would the view of an actual object at that position in the real world. Ideally this includes the effects of parallax, occlusion-of and occlusion-by real objects, and size of virtual objects as the head moves closer or further from the defined position of the virtual object in the real world. In order to calculate the transformations for these effects it is necessary for the AR system to simultaneously track the position of real world objects and the changes in the position of the head. This Simultaneous Location and Mapping (SLAM) functionality is provided by software SDK's such ARToolkit to derive these transformations using computer vision algorithms on scenes captured by cameras and other sensors such as depth of field sensors.

USAGE SCENARIOS OF AR MANUFACTURING

Provision of in situ instructions
An important aspect of manufacturing is the provision of *guidance and instructions* on the details of steps in carrying out manual procedures. This is necessary for the training of new staff, or existing staff after changes in workflows, for the case of complicated and variable workflows, for the case of exception conditions in the workflow, and especially for periodic or unplanned maintenance. Historically these instructions have been provided in paper based instruction manuals and guides. With the advent of computer terminals in the workspace, these instructions became more multimedia based – including the use of photos, videos and 2D and 3D animations (Smith & Athwal, 1995). The provision of these instructions becomes particularly powerful when they are available in situ and at the time when the task or procedure is to be carried out. Thus, the operative can flick through the instruction manual or view videos on a tablet or other screen at the workplace and complete the task immediately afterwards.
AR takes this process to the next stage by overlaying the instructions, videos, animations, etc. that seem to appear on virtual screens directly in the real working environment. These can be supplemented by, for example, the AR system locating and highlighting real parts that need to be worked on with instructions next to them or animations demonstrating virtual representations of these parts being manipulated in the required manner. In this scenario, using video see through (VST) AR, would involve the operative holding up a tablet and viewing the real scene (via the tablet's rear facing camera) with real time composited virtual elements on its screen. However this has the disadvantage of the operative's hands being occupied when they could be used to directly carry out the instructions. One solution to this problem is to have the screen included in a HMD; and indeed this is possible with modified VR HMD's such that

they include cameras close to the positions of the user's eyes. However this camera-mediated view of the world is limited by the resolutions in pixel size, colour depth and contrast of the cameras and display, and the current state of art in AR HMDs is to use optical see through (OST) which are able to provide the user with an unencumbered natural view of the real world in all its glory.

FIGURE 1: motionEAP system for manual assembly work using in-situ projection to provide assembly instructions using motion recognition (Funk, Kosch, Kettner, Korn, & Schmidt, 2016)

The HMD can be linked to cloud based enterprise databases and tracking systems to deliver the right information at the right moment directly into an operative's line of sight, while leaving their hands free so they can work without interruption. This dramatically reduces the time needed to complete a job because there is no need to flip through a paper manual or consult a workstation. Errors can be reduced and compliance with standard operating procedures assured as AR can display explicit guidance overlaid on the work being done and track completion of required steps. An additional functionality provided in current examples is the capability to connect by video with remote experts to share what is seen by the operative and get real-time assistance.

FIGURE 2: Assembly instructions being displayed in a Smart Factory environment (Paelke, 2014)

A number of studies have demonstrated substantial improvements in productivity using the methods outlined above: Boeing showed that AR improved productivity in wiring harness assembly by 25%; GE Healthcare showed that warehouse workers could complete a new picklist order 46% faster when using AR rather than a paper list and work station. Additional cases from GE and several other firms show an average productivity improvement of 32%.

Augmented reality overlays on existing real world scenes
Another powerful usage scenario in manufacturing is the capability for the AR system to give the impression that additional virtual structures are overlaid onto actual floors, walls and machinery. One use is to directly visualise planned changes of configuration or additions of

new machines to the assembly line or workspace. The new machines are displayed as virtual objects that appear to be in the designed positions within the real workshop; then these virtual objects can be manipulated to take into account any constraints that are observed in the visualisation and these transformations can be immediately captured by the AR system to feedback into the re-design process. The user can move around the new machines or workspaces and physically check for safety and general ergonomic considerations. This scenario can be extended to allow operators to be presented with virtual hazard conditions to safely practice avoidance and compensatory patterns and behaviours.

FIGURE 3: Example of video-mixed display used in a manufacturing environment (Fraga-Lamas, Fernandez-Carames, Blanco-Novoa, & Vilar-Montesinos, 2018)

An interesting use case in this scenario is to test the suitability of human working with cooperative robots (cobots) whereby AR is used to present the cobot as an animated virtual object and the user can interact with the virtual cobot to carry out tasks using additional virtual objects. A further advantage of the AR approach here is the opportunity to practice these interactions without the danger of physical harm from mistakes in cobot or human performance.

The same overlay capability can be used to provide so-called "x-ray vision" whereby hidden parts and structures (eg pipes or wiring within walls, or internal parts of equipment that might be difficult to access) can be overlaid as virtual objects directly in situ onto the normally visible walls and covers of the real world-view. This allows planning of where access is best made or better understanding of operation of machinery to plan maintenance or enhancement.

Visualisation of product details and designs

AR is going to change the way product designers create their products and the way end consumers purchase them by enhancing visualisation, product design and brand engagement (Scholz & Duffy, 2018). Unlike VR, AR offers a new layer of information into the user's current environment, offering the possibility to showcase design processes in the place they are meant to be. Within product design AR enables the instant sharing and visualisation of CAD models, bringing them to life in 3D potentially at real scale and in their eventual environment with the option for designers to interact directly with the models to make and capture design changes. However conversion of CAD models to virtual objects is not trivial; for example CAD models could be at too high a resolution to allow real-time rendering and manipulation. These issues can be resolved by use of intermediate file formats (such as .STL and .STP) and appropriate workflows (see e.g. Lorenz et al. 2015). This AR use case is an example of expanding the capabilities of product designers and engineers.

Companies like Adobe, Autodesk and PTC are also currently exploring the possibilities of AR in the shared design and visualisation area, creating new tools that will change the way designers work with their products, enabling collaborative immersive design, visualisation and navigation of virtual products in real spaces.

FIGURE 4: Air-Modelling tool for gesture based modelling in AR (Arroyave-Tobón, Osorio-Gómez, & Cardona-McCormick, 2015)

It is not only designers and product engineers who will benefit from this, the use of AR is likely going to change the way customers buy online, with renowned companies like IKEA or Inditex providing AR tools for visualizing augmented versions of their products in users' houses using dedicated mobile apps. Additionally, new software development tools are enabling customers to take real time accurate measurements of their spaces by using built-in mobile cameras, offering a full solution for virtually measuring and furnishing spaces, making sure the layout is what the consumer expected before purchasing it. In a B2B scenario this capability offers manufacturers the opportunity to show how their product could be integrated in situ as a component or enhancement to their customers' existing machinery, assembly or environment.

Operator training

AR offers an invaluable opportunity for changing the delivery, efficiency and quality of operator training and presents the potential for redefining future training environments (Jetter 2018). Common to other applications of AR, notably in design and visualisation, virtual content can augment the real environment in varying different forms. These can reflect different training parameters bespoke to the training operation. These visualisations can be animated and updated in real-time providing dynamic training programmes which are adaptable and personalised in ways not feasible with traditional real environments.

Current applications for AR training often present the AR virtual content as overlays that facilitate the training program by presenting in-view visual instructions, alternative training guidance (i.e. in view directions and task indicators), training feedback (i.e. visual guidance of task success, failures or length/difficulty of training) and also training parameters (i.e. task specific attributes such as the names of components and physical properties of virtual objects). This improved level of interactive information creates a richer training environment and furthermore supports the redesign of new training programmes. The benefit that AR brings has been illustrated in many studies to improve the overall training experience for users, improve training accuracy and overall reduce the cognitive task load throughout the training exercise.

FIGURE 5: In-view visual instructions for a bespoke assembly training at BMW (Werrlich, Nitsche, & Notni, 2017)

In addition to improving the visualisation within operator training, AR also poses the potential for creating collaborative training environments. These environments can support the coworking of multiple users in real-time or even present an AR representation of coworking with robots (or cobots) in a hazard free environment.

These training environments can also support the real time interaction of co-workers who are either spatially co-located (i.e. multiple trainees using the same environment) or remote (i.e. in different sites or geographically separated). This can create training environments where trainees can support co-workers in collaborative training or be managed and assisted by facilitators who interact with the trainee in real time. Current AR devices (e.g. Hololens and Meta2) often support multimodal methods of interaction (i.e. hand gestures, voice control, eye gaze etc.). These interaction modes can be used to not only interact with the AR content but to also offer communication to other trainees or facilitators in real-time. Thus AR can present a collaborative two way interactive communication channel whereby a facilitator can give voice instructions to a trainee, a trainee can report back on task difficulties or form a communication channel between collaborative trainees. This form of collaborative AR is effective in highlighting how users can mutually interact within training environments and also establish routines to solving complex collaborative problems.

CURRENT CHALLENGES AND LIMITATIONS

Fundamental early reviews of AR technology (Azuma, A survey of augmented reality, 1997) (Azuma, et al., 2001) highlighted some key limitations, namely inaccurate tracking, cumbersome and heavy displays, lack of portability and inaccurate depth perception. While some of these early problems have largely improved due to the vast technological advances in recent years (i.e. display quality, tracking, rendering and device portability), however many challenges and fundamental problems in different aspects AR technology still exist and can limit potential industry application. These problems can be categorised as technical problems (i.e. relating to the inherent technical limitations of the hardware), interface problems (i.e. relating to the interaction method and the overall interface between the user and the AR content) and perceptual problems (i.e. relating to the overall perception and realism of the augmented content).

Technical limitations refer to the impact of technological shortcomings in hardware, which can directly impact the user's quality of experience or the overall effectiveness of the AR solution. For example, low resolution tracking sensors can cause environment segmentation errors, augmentation difficulties and thus result in a poor representation of the virtual content (i.e. objects may appear flat, in the wrong location, or jitter around their fixed locations). Latency is a further technical limitation that can impair the overall user experience and reliability of the AR solution. Latency in the rendering and tracking can cause a static virtual objects to move about its fixed position ('jumpiness'), whereas latency in the interaction response can result in the virtual object movement being delayed causing a poor user quality of experience and thus a detachment from the application.

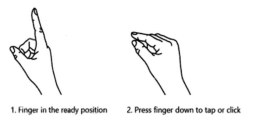

1. Finger in the ready position   2. Press finger down to tap or click

FIGURE 6: HoloLens Air Tap gesture interaction (Microsoft, 2016)

Interface limitations relate to the overall level of direct interaction that the user has with the augmented content and the interface the system provides. Currently there are no defined standards for facilitating the overall interaction between the user and the virtual content, therefore the interaction devices or methods used by one device may not be common to alternative devices, thus presenting problems for application development and porting of applications to different devices. Furthermore, while some hardware devices support hand interactions between the users and the augmented content, these are often gesture based (e.g. the air tap and bloom in the HoloLens) and do not reflect the full dexterity offered by real interactions with real objects (i.e. the user cannot grasp virtual objects the same as they would with real objects). This can present limitations in the design of the system and not reflect the interactions that are needed within the real industrial situation.

For example, in an assembly training scenario a user may be trained to assemble augmented components using gestures that do not relate to the interactions they would have with the real components in the practical assembly task. These issues are being addressed by the current and ongoing development of AR systems that employ more natural grasp based hand interactions (Al-Kalbani et-al 2016, 2017)

FIGURE 7: Freehand grasping interaction (Frutos-Pascual, Al-Kalbani, Dolhasz, & Williams, 2017)

Perceptual problems relate to the overall user perception of the augmented system and this often relates to the visual clarity of the augmented content. The current limited field of view (FOV) in hardware is another fundamental perceptual and technical problem. FOV limitations restrict how much of the augmented world is perceived and viewable by the user from a given viewpoint, thus making visual based interactions potentially cumbersome for users to perform. Finally, properties of the display device, such as luminance, contrast and resolution can also negatively impact perception of the augmented content. Notably the brightness of the display device may be suitable for dimly lit real environments but can be compromised in highly lit (or external) environments.

CONCLUSIONS

Numerous studies have demonstrated proven benefits for the use of AR in many aspects of the manufacturing workflow. The most prevalent current trend for the delivery of AR is via the use of Smart Glasses and Head Mounted Devices, with the latter providing greater functionality. Significant investments are being made by industry giants and specialist suppliers to continue to provide ever more capable and comfortable devices, with some commentators believing that in the long term such devices may even come into general use to supplant smartphones. Thus the time is ripe for manufacturing companies to start pilot programmes to develop and tailor AR systems to meet their particular demands. They should do this with the confidence that, as they become ready to roll out these AR assisted workflows more fully into the enterprise, more powerful and/or cheaper hardware and software solutions should be available to enable achievement of significant ROI.

References

Al-Kalbani, M., Williams, I. & Frutos-Pascual, M., 2016. Analysis of Medium Wrap Freehand Virtual Object Grasping in Exocentric Mixed Reality. 2016 IEEE International Symposium on Mixed and Augmented Reality (ISMAR).

Al-Kalbani, M., Frutos-Pascual, M. & Williams, I., 2017. Freehand grasping in mixed reality: analysing variation during transition phase of interaction. Proceedings of the 19th ACM International Conference on Multimodal Interaction - ICMI 2017.

Arroyave-Tobón, S., Osorio-Gómez, G., & Cardona-McCormick, J. (2015). AIR-MODELLING: A tool for gesture-based solid modelling in context during early design stages in AR environments. Computers in Industry, 73-81.

Azuma, R. (1997). A survey of augmented reality. Presence: Teleoperators & Virtual Environments, 355-385.

Azuma, R., Baillot, Y., Behringer, R., Feiner, S., Julier, S., & MacIntyre, B. (2001). Recent advances in augmented reality. Washington DC: Naval Research Lab.

Fraga-Lamas, P., Fernandez-Carames, T., Blanco-Novoa, O., & Vilar-Montesinos, M. (2018). A Review on Industrial Augmented Reality Systems for the Industry 4.0 Shipyard. SPECIAL SECTION ON HUMAN-CENTERED SMART SYSTEMS AND TECHNOLOGIES.

Frutos-Pascual, M., Al-Kalbani, M., Dolhasz, A., & Williams, I. (2017). A Freehand Natural Interaction System for Mixed Reality Healthcare Demonstration. WIN Annual Conference. Warwick.

Funk, M., Kosch, T., Kettner, R., Korn, O., & Schmidt, A. (2016). Motioneap: An overview of 4 years of combining industrial assembly with augmented reality for industry 4.0. Proceedings of the 16th international conference on knowledge technologies and datadriven business.

Jetter J, Eimecke J, Rese A, Augmented reality tools for industrial applications: What are potential key performance indicators and who benefits?,Computers in Human Behavior,Volume 87,2018,Pages 18-33,ISSN 0747-5632,

Lorenz M, Spranger M, Riedel T, Pürzel F, Wittstock V, Klimant P. CAD to VR–A Methodology for the Automated Conversion of Kinematic CAD Models to Virtual Reality. Procedia CIRP, 2016; 41: 358–363.

Microsoft. (2016). HoloLens Gesture Control. Obtenido de https://docs.microsoft.com/en-us/windows/mixed-reality/gestures

Paelke, V. (2014). Augmented reality in the smart factory: Supporting workers in an industry 4.0. environment. Emerging Technology and Factory Automation (ETFA), 2014 IEEE.

Scholz, J., & Duffy, K. (2018). We ARe at home: How augmented reality reshapes mobile marketing and consumer-brand relationships. Journal of Retailing and Consumer Services, 11-23.

Smith, M., & Athwal, C. (1995). A Study of the Use of Cost Effective Multimedia in a Manufacturing Environment. Advances in Manufacturing Technology (p. 749). Taylor & Francis.

Werrlich, S., Nitsche, K., & Notni, G. (2017). Demand Analysis for an Augmented Reality based Assembly Training. Proceedings of the 10th International Conference on PErvasive Technologies Related to Assistive Environments.

Smart Die Casting: A New Approach

Adel Aneiba[1] and Stephen Brown[2]

[1]School of Computing and Digital Technology,
Birmingham City University.
Adel.aneiba@bcu.ac.uk
[2]Meridian Lightweight Technologies United Kingdom
Sutton-In-Ashfield, Nottingham,
sbrown@meridian-mag.com

Abstract

HPDC (High Pressure Die-casting) is one of the core manufacturing processes of the industrial revolution and is currently still valid for many industry sectors such as automotive. With the current competitive markets, there is a need to improve the HPDC process to meet the high demands from many Original Equipment Manufacturers (OEM). Therefore, this chapter reviews the state of the art in the die casting domain and related elements. In addition, it will provide an innovative approach to enhance and optimise the HPDC process using smart technologies. Optimizing the HPDC process is a key task for increasing productivity and reducing defective parts (e.g. scrap ratio). An overview of the HPDC process is provided with more attention to the most common defects and their sources. This chapter reviews the work that has been carried out by the researchers in this domain and identifies the main factors that affect the process. It also identifies how to maintain consistency in trying to reach the "zero-defect" production status. It does this by looking at real-time process control mechanisms and understanding the various process variables and their impact on end product quality.

Keywords

HPDC Process, Smart Sensing, Process Parameters Optimisation, Adaptive Learning

INTRODUCTION

The high pressure die casting process is a manufacturing process used to form metals such as aluminium, zinc and magnesium into different geometric shapes by melting and pushing the metal under high pressure into a cavity or mould (Vinarcik, 2003). Common pressures that are used to fill the cavity at higher solidification are between 20-120 MPa, which lead to high speed filling rates that are usually 25-60 m/s and can exceed more than 80 m/s. At these pressures the molten metal filling time is very short, at about 0.01- 0.2 seconds, depending on the size and design of the cast (Bonollo *et al*, 2015; Gariboldi *et al,* 2010).

High-pressure die casting (HPDC) is mainly appropriate for high production rates. For example, in the automotive industry, 60% of components are created using HPDC. It is well known that HPDC with a low cycle time is particularly suitable when high production rates are required. The scrap rate in a very efficient environment should not exceed 5% or the sequence will be costly to the manufacturer, who may pass on this inefficiency as part of their overhead. As these casting requirements get considerably larger and more complex the industry in general can often get into difficulties trying to keep these inefficiencies under control. The goal is the same as most manufacturing, to try and maintain consistent casting quality from the first part to the last, to the benefit of the manufacturer, the customer and quality production part delivery times (Bonollo *et al* 2015). One of the limitations of HPDC is that the overall complex process is not managed by a single information system, and the systems we do find in place are often not accurate enough to provide efficient diagnosis of the immediate issue: if this happens it may involve a stoppage and a loss of heat in the die, which is a major contributor to the inefficiencies mentioned. The heat map within the die, that is set during the development of the part, needs to remain consistent to ensure that each casting regularly and consistently fills the cavity of the die in the same manner as its predecessor. If the heat map in the die is erratic then the metal will flow erratically and introduce irregularities into the process. In many cases controls only measure machine parameters, whilst the temperature of the holding furnace, for example, is controlled separately. In other words, there is no holistic view for the entire production system, especially the cavity heat in real time.

Therefore, there is a need to have a holistic computerized approach in place to monitor and control the entire HPDC process parameters, permitting them to be corrected or optimized to produce high quality parts and get closer to achieving "zero-defect" production status. Despite the fact that most HPDC machines are equipped with sensors that measure basic process data such as hydraulic pressure or piston velocity, these readings are not correlated with other process parameters to validate the method. For example, if the filling time varied only in the range of milliseconds because of piston velocity, then there would be an impact on content and location of defects. Monitoring various parameters such as temperature in different locations within the cavity during the die casting process, in the holding furnace and in the ladle or the level of hydrogen are very important when targeting the consistencies necessary for continued quality part production.

This die casting process takes various high precision steps in a very short time for mass production, as seen in Figure 1. The quality of the parts produced depends on all of these parameters being consistent to the original parameter settings arrived at during development of a good part. Achieving this refined process is very important to both producers and customers. Reducing any inconsistencies in this process is an essential task to keep improving the process to drive down scrap and supply to ever changing market demand. Many changes occur in process variables throughout the casting life cycle. These changes will have an impact on the die cast part quality. This chapter will review the latest research work in this area and propose some directions that can be adopted to enhance the die casting process. The quality of die cast is based upon several factors including material failure, construction errors, variations of process parameters and the surrounding environment. The effect of the material not just determines the properties of the final casting, but also impacts the machine and tooling (Patel *et al*, 2017).

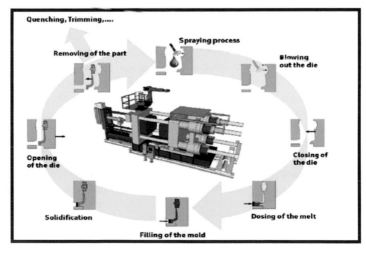

FIGURE 1: The HDPC Process Cycle (Bonollo *et al* 2015)

There are two major high pressure die casting processes in the die-casting industry, they are called: cold chamber and hot chamber. Each process has its own characteristics, purpose and mechanism. For example, Figure 2 illustrates the cold chamber Die Casting type. The main different between cold and hot is that, cold chamber die casting is a preferred manufacturing process for metal alloys that have high melting points such as aluminium, brass and copper (Patel *et al* , 2017; Winkler *et al*, 2015). In addition, cold chamber die casting can take few seconds to solidify. Furthermore, cold chambers are usually made to have multiple cavities, so different machine parts can be produced at the same time.

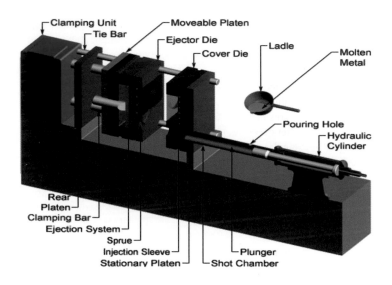

FIGURE 2: Basic Cold Chamber Die Casting (Customoartnet, 2018)

Meridian currently develop and manufacture magnesium parts for the automotive sector via High Pressure Die-Casting (HDPC) using the cold chamber method. In order to meet the demand of end user requirements and to improve current manufacturing methods, Meridian are constantly looking to optimise and improve their process to produce more cost effective products and reduce the amount of variability in order to reduce scrap. Die temperature distribution commonly seen in a production die is ~100-150 C^{o} across the die face, and these are often required to manage the material flow through the complex geometry in an effective manner to produce a good part. These parameters are developed and finalised at the development stage, and once the heat map requirement is established this must remain as constant as possible throughout the production. However, there are a multitude of factors that can affect these temperatures and any one of these factors can affect the visual quality and fill integrity.

Reliable temperatures within die casting tools are crucial for flawless results of the die casting process, and accordingly, release agents and their corresponding method of application can play an important role. Die surface temperature is crucial for high quality, efficiency and faultless component manufacture. Many of the defects seen in the traditional HPDC system, such as shrinkage, porosity, cracks, and blisters, are caused by out-of-control die temperatures (Podprocká *et al*, 2015). To mitigate this, it is mandatory to monitor the die casting process, in real time and without interruption to the production cycle, the die temperature surface and related spray effect. Higher or lower die temperatures can also have a negative impact on tool life, start up and cycle time, as well as energy consumption and maintenance costs due to unnecessary use of thermal regulation, air pressure, and/or water based lubricant (Bonollo *et al*, 2015).

Business Challenge
In any die casting industry, the quality of the produced parts from the die-casting process is crucial. If the produced parts have defects or impurities as a result of an inefficient die casting process, then more process steps are needed, such as trimming and puffing. An initial investigation conducted at Meridian Ltd found that the majority of defects could be traced to the problems stated below.

According to a chief engineer at a UK-based die casting foundry, the main problem affecting the die causing it to not function properly and produce a high rate of scrap parts is heat variations and heat distribution rate inside and outside the die cavity. This problem affects solidification and flow patterns in the mould and ultimately the quality of the end product. As the die opens and closes after every "shot" that is taken then we are bound to see temperature fluctuations, but if these regular opening and closing stages are managed and consistent then the temperature variations from the required parameters remain controlled to the values expected and necessary for good production conditions, as set during the development phases. However, any unexpected stoppages, for a multitude of reasons, which disrupt this pattern of opening and closing will tend to also disrupt the temperature pattern, and in turn cause an increase in potential scrap parts.

The system presently being used to monitor temperatures relies on expensive thermocouple solutions that can only be deployed well below the surface of the die cavity due to the pressures seen at the die surface (over 3000T on existing machines). The time taken for the "true" heat of the die cavity surface to register at the thermocouple cannot be controlled by solid state due to the erratic nature of the temperature variables. But, a truly predictive system that can monitor the actual temperature of the die cavity surface in "real time" would be invaluable to the predictive control of the process. Once an issue is identified then the solution could be sought before it causes disruption to the process and the parts being cast. This system could then be used to investigate and deploy a solution to the temperature issue before a stoppage is needed.

Currently, a semi-manual process is being employed to control the liquid flow melting rate using manual valves to cool down (using water) or heat up (using oil) through ingress cooling/heating channels. Not only is an excessive scrap rate consequently produced, but also the type, size and diagnosis of the defects can vary. In fact, the process itself is extremely delay-sensitive, therefore, without adequate statistical process control, is clearly inefficient. In order to produce high volumes of precision parts, however, other factors that can contribute to the die cavity heat distribution should be considered:

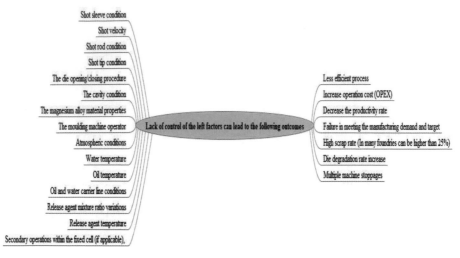

FIGURE 3: Die Casting Process Parameters and Their Effects

Finally, the recycling process of the defective automotive parts is very costly and time consuming. Based on the above, the need for a solution for this problem or even an improvement of the current process by reducing the scrap rate by a sufficient percentage is a must. In addition, by performing these enhancement actions, Die-Casting foundries could achieve a more mature and efficient relationship with large end users.

RELATED WORK

Research and development in the area of die casting is limited but there are some reasonable efforts made by the research community around the globe in an attempt to tackle the challenges that arise in this domain. Swillo *et al*, (2013) presents imaging based approaches and neural network techniques to capture and categorize surface defects during inspection of cast parts. Based on several conditions, such as processing techniques, castings might produce surface discontinuities, such as cracks and lack of fill, that greatly impact the material's properties. The developed vision system uses an advanced image processing algorithm based on modified Laplacian of Gaussian edge detection method. In addition, neural network techniques have been used to detect three groups of defects: namely blowholes, shrinkage porosity and shrinkage cavity.

Bonollo *et al*, (2015) have reviewed the most relevant challenges for the HPDC industry that prevent ''zero-defect'' production. This includes investigation of the real-time process control concept and realizing the role of the HDPC process variables and process optimization. They suggest that the breakthrough for the HPDC industry is the change from a simple input setup to dynamic total quality management. Winkler *et al* (2015) have produced an intelligent cognitive system taking all quality controlling parameters into account to reduce the scrap rates in Aluminium high pressure die casting. Their solution has used advanced sensors to monitor new process parameters, such as the sound of the shot and pressure sensors inside the cavity. The collected sensors data have been stored in a database for further analysis. The data is then used to obtain correlations between process parameters and quality characteristics in Aluminium high pressure die casting. This research work has added real value to the public domain by demonstrating the effects of incorporating smart devices into traditional processes. The system described was validated using a simulation tool called MAGMASOFT (MG, 2018). An adaptive learning technique was adopted as the cognitive system for improving the process over time.

Haokai & Peijie, (2016) have developed a remote monitoring system for die casting scenarios. The developed monitoring system uses sensing equipment for real-time monitoring. The system is connected to remote client computers through industrial networks. Patel *et al* (2017) have studied a number of types of process for HPDC, such as cold chamber die casting and hot chamber die casting. In addition, they have identified the major problems which occur during the processing of metal alloys, especially aluminium. They state that casting defects are caused from material failure, construction errors or as an effect of process parameters.

Ignaszak *et al*, (2015) focus on the issue of discontinuity in the die casting process and in particular in the filling phase. The compactness of their structure is not perfect; the discontinuities present in these castings can be classified as porosity, that is shrinkage and gas (hydrogen and gas-air occlusions) in origin. The mixed gas and shrinkage nature of porosity makes it difficult to identify and indicate the dominant source. Using the "density index" - DI to estimate the amount of hydrogen in the melted alloy, is an important step in identifying the correct amount of heat needed to melt the alloy. This will help to improve the filling process.

Adke *et al*, (2014) have used the Taguchi method for design of experiment (DOE) to optimise pressure die-casting process parameters and identify the optimal tuning for improving the cycle time. There are four major HDPC process machine parameters: namely melting temperature, injection pressure, plunger speed and cooling phase. Sequences of experiments have been conducted to identify the optimal process parameters to produce high quality products. Their findings suggest that the following parameter values (Cycle time is 34 sec for Melting Temp 700 °C, Injection Pressure 900 bar, Plunger speed 3m/s & cooling time 8 sec) give optimum performance for control of porosity. Hangai *et al*, (2014) have proposed two types of fractal analyses to illustrate porosity in terms of the shape of individual pores and the three-dimensional distribution of multiple cracks.

DIE-CASTING DEFECTS AND THEIR ORIGINS

The complexity of the die casting process stems from the fact that the entire process is controlled by multiple variables. These can be environmental factors or process parameters. In order to produce a high quality cast part with almost "Zero defects"; these factors and parameters need to be optimised and controlled. Therefore, it is essential to identify them and find an efficient way to measure and optimise them for the benefit of die casters and OEMs. Bonollo *et al*, 2015 have classified the most common defects (surface defects, internal and surface defects, and geometrical defects) and their source as shown in Table 1. Clearly, from the table shrinkage, Gas-related and Filling related are the most common defects, therefore, there is a clear need to pay more attention to these for current and future solutions.

TABLE 1: Classification of HPDC defects and frequency of occurrence (Bonollo et al, 2015)

Defect subclass	Frequency of Occurrence(%)	Predictable by Simulation?	Experimental validation	Monitoring parameter
Shrinkage defects	20	Only partially	X-Rays, Microscopy	Temperature, pressure, metal front sensors
Gas-related defects	15	No	No X-Rays, Microscopy, blister test	Air pressure, humidity
Filling related defects	35	Yes	Visual inspection, leakage tests	Air pressure, metal front sensors, temperature
Undesired phases	5	No	Microscopy	Shot chamber sensoring
Thermal contraction defects	5	Yes	Visual inspection, Microscopy	Temperature
Metal-die interaction defects	5	Only partially	Microscopy	Temperature, ejection force
Out of tolerance	5	By advanced simulation	Visual inspection, Metrology	Geometry measures
Lack of material	5	Yes	Visual inspection, Metrology	Geometry measures
Excess of material, flash	5	By advanced simulation	Visual inspection, Metrology	Geometry measures

For example, the major defects for the rejections during production were identified as shrinkages, inclusions, porosity/gas holes and cracks. The factors that influence the formation of shrinkage cavities are shown in Table 2.

TABLE 2: illustrates the major defects for the rejections during production

Metal Quality	Pouring Condition	Die Condition	Casting Parameter	Molten Metal Quality
-Solidification range -Shrinkage during solidification	-Pouring temperature -Rate of pouring Feeding systems	-Initial temperature of the die. -Conductivity of the die.	-Thickness Shape.	-Inclusion content

SMART DIE-CASTING: THE NEW APPROACH

As mentioned earlier that the most relevant challenges for die casting industry are: ''zero-defect'' production, real-time process control, understanding the role of process variables, and process optimization, therefore a holistic approach should be considered as a foundation for any solution (Bonollo *et al*, 2015). Many factors, parameters and variables have an impact on the produced automotive part as a result of the die casting process. The aim of this approach is to develop a novel smart solution to maintain the thermal and flow process parameters for the melted magnesium material inside the die cast mould, in order to manufacture high precision die cast products. Key areas to address include, heating and cooling of the die, developing real-time temperature mapping of the heat distribution in the die with associated control measures, and development and validation of a simulation model.

A site visit and interview with a leading magnesium die caster in the UK has been conducted to understand the environment of the die casting process, capture the requirements and carry out essential analysis for the proposed solution (See Figure 4). The concept of distributed control systems can be adopted and applied as a possible solution (with a certain degree of modifications and customization) into the magnesium die casting process. Historically, this type of control systems fall under Industrial Control Systems (ICSs) where several subcategories can be identified such as Supervisory Control and Data Acquisition (SCADA) systems, Distributed Control Systems (DCS), and other smaller control system configurations such as skid-mounted Programmable Logic Controllers (PLC). These systems share several common characteristics and patterns from sensing, data collection, data communication, data processing and control.

It is necessary to develop a probing/sensing method to measure temperature and other process parameters like pressure and filling velocity, in order to sustain the required heat distribution inside the die cavity zones. This will require real time measurements for the heat distribution rate and the capability of adjusting the temperature accordingly. In case of variation inside the die cavity, the system will capture this and instantly trigger an actuator to release the right amount of Heating or Cooling by actuating (opening or closing) an appropriate valve to maintain the melting flow rate of the metal (e.g. magnesium). To make the system more efficient, the die cast chamber will be equipped with various types of sensors to capture the required parameters.

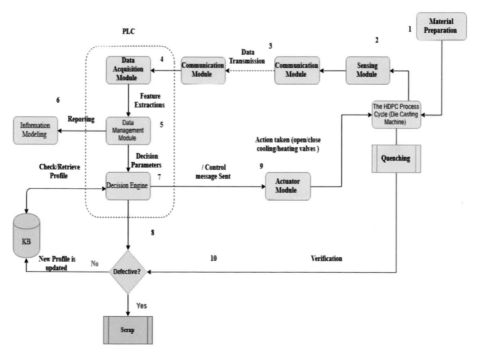

FIGURE 4: Smart Die Casting (SDC) Model

The system should predict the possible defect or defects and reduce the amount of excess scrap. This can be done by developing a novel intelligent algorithm (i.e. adaptive learning technique), for predicting the condition of the part being manufactured using a real-time multi-sensing system. Self-adaptation behaviour is key for self-automation and to reduce human intervention as much as possible. It is important to mitigate any variation of the liquid metal temperature as it has a direct effect on the quality of the produced part. Obtaining the optimal parameters for mitigating a particular defect is a real challenge as different die casting parts have different optimized parameters.

SDC MODEL COMPONENTS

The model for the proposed solution (See Figure 4) has eight modules working together to achieve the aim of this project:

Sensing module
Advanced sensors will be used and applied to the HPDC machine process. This could be contact or non-contact sensors, it all depends on the outcomes of the current investigation. This module will allow the continuous control of the process itself, monitoring and recording the evolution of all related variables during the casting cycle.

Communication module
The communication module provides the required connectivity to send data from the sensing module to the controller and sending control messages from the controller to the actuator module (closed loop).

Data acquisition
The data acquisition module is a process of sampling signals that measure real physical conditions of the die cast machine and convert the resulting samples into digital numeric values (i.e. Analog-to-digital converters, to convert conditioned sensor signals to digital values) that can be manipulated by the following module.

Data processing and analytics module

- Filtering /Classification
- Correlations

Information modelling module

- Dashboard (e.g. Heat Map)
- Reporting
- Analysis (Simulation Model)

Decision making module
At this stage, the processed data from the previous module will be treated as inputs for the developed algorithm (statistical /mathematical model) to be considered for its calculations and produce an output in form of numerical values that represent what is called a "correction profile ". This can then be matched to one in the knowledgebase if it exists or to generate a new profile for the current case of the die, in either case, to be executed instantly based on a prediction process. The outcome is then verified, and if the desired outcome is achieved, the newly produced profile will be stored in the knowledgebase for later use.

PLC Module
The PLC module will be responsible for controlling the heating/cooling valves by sending a control message to the actuators. The actuators in this case will be a group of electric valves that control the water flow for the cooling process and the oil flow for the heating process. The PLC based system will use wireless technology (i.e. ZigBee) to interface with sensors that interact with the die casting machine.

Actuators module
This module is responsible for actuating (opening or closing) a valve. Power-operated actuators will be used to allow the valve to be adjusted remotely. Power-operated valve actuators may be the final elements of an automatic control loop which automatically regulates the water and oil flows. An actuator requires a control signal that is sent by the PLC module as well as a source of power.

CONCLUSIONS

The die-casting process is a complex engineering manufacturing process, whereby understanding the process thoroughly is key to providing a suitable solution for any defect that may happen during the operation phase. Tuning the plunger speed to allow molten metal filling the sprue at low speed and filling the mould at high speed is best practice. Preventing the surrounding air from entering into the die by closing the gate quickly and increasing the pressure helps to reduce porosity defects. Installing advanced sensors in the domain of the HPDC machine to monitor and control the HPDC process in real time is essential, in order to gain insights into process parameters for producing good quality cast parts. Efficient heat distribution must be achieved within the cavity by controlling the amount of heating/cooling flow over the time of the die casting production phase. From this review, it is clear that multidisciplinary research and development work is needed to employ and test new technologies (e.g. deep learning and smart sensing) that may help to enhance the quality of the die casting in wider manufacturing processes and HPDC scenarios. Finally, there is no doubt that innovation support is needed in HPDC foundries, as in most cases they do not have sufficient scientific and technological capacity to design and develop such innovative solutions.

References

Adke, M., N., Karanjkar, S.V, (2014). Optimization of die-casting process parameters to identify optimized level for cycle time using Taguchi method, ISSN: 2319 – 1058, Volume 4 Issue 4 December, PP: 375.

Bonollo, F., Fiorese, E., Timelli, G., Arnberg,L., and Adamane, A.C.R. (2014). StaCast project: From a survey of European aluminum alloys foundries to new standards on defect classification and on mechanical potential of casting alloys, 71st World Foundry Congress, Spain

Bonollo, F., Gramegna, N. and Timelli, G. (2015). High-Pressure Die-Casting: Contradictions and Challenges, Article in JOM: The journal of the Minerals, Metals & Materials Society , Springer, ISSN 1047-4838, Volume 67, Number 5

CustomPartNet, (2018). Die Casting Process, Available at: http://www.custompartnet.com/wu/die-casting, accessed on 15 August 2018

Garibaldi, E., Bonollo, F., and Parona, P. (2010) Handbook of Defects in HPDC, 1st ed. (Milano: Associazione Italiana di Metallurgia, 2010)

Hangai, Y. Kitahara, S. (2008). Quantitative Evaluation of Porosity in Aluminum Die Castings by Fractal Analysis of Perimeter, Materials Transactions, Vol. 49, No. 4 (2008), pp: 782 to 786.

Haokai, H.; Peijie, L; (2016). Design of remote monitor system for die casting units, 2nd International Conference on Control Science and Systems Engineering (ICCSSE), Singapore, 2016, pp. 252-255.

Ignaszak, Z., Hajkowski, J. (2015). Contribution to the Identification of Porosity Type in AlSiCu High-Pressure-Die-Castings by Experimental and Virtual Way, ISSN (1897-3310) Volume 15, Issue 1/2015, PP: 143 – 151.

MG, Magma Simulation Software, available from: https://www.magmasoft.com/en/solutions/magmasoft/, accessed on 29/07/2018.

Mulla, J.G. Potdar V.V., Swapnil, Kulkarni, S. (2014). Investigating die casting process parameters to identify the optimized levels using taguchi methods for design of experiment (doe), ISSN2249–8974, PP: 160-162.

Patel, J.M., Pandya, Y. R., Sharma, D. and Patel, R.C. (2017). Various Type of Defects on Pressure Die Casting for Aluminium Alloys, IJSRD - International Journal for Scientific Research & Development| Vol. 5, Issue 01, 2017 ISSN (online): 2321-0613

Podprocká, R., Malik, J., and Bolibruchová, D. (2015). Defects in high pressure die casting process, Manufacturing Technology Journal.

Swillo, S.J., Perzyk, M. (2013). Surface Casting Defects Inspection Using Vision System and Neural Network Techniques, ISSN (1897-3310)Volume 13, Issue 4/2013,PP:103 – 106.

Vinarcik, E.J., (2003). High Integrity Die Casting Processes, 1st ed, New York: Wiley, pp. 3–25, 145–156.

Winkler, M., Kallien, L., and Feyertag, T. (2015). Correlation between process parameters and quality characteristics in aluminum high pressure die casting, NADCA Conference, 2015.

A Review Of Computational Fluid Dynamics Methods For High Pressure Die Casting

Dominic Flynn and Abed Alaswad

School of Engineering and the Built Environment, Birmingham City University, Birmingham, UK.

Email: {Dominic.Flynn, Abed.alaswad}@bcu.ac.uk

Abstract

The automotive industry is increasingly using lightweight materials aiming to achieve vehicle fuel economy, less pollution, and better drivability and performance. In this regard, Magnesium with nearly half the weight of aluminium, offers great potential. However, due to a number of technical and commercial obstacles, Magnesium was not been promoted effectively in the past compared with Steel and Aluminium industries. High Pressure Die Casting (HPDC) is a manufacturing process that is essential to make components for the automotive industry and widely employed for casting magnesium products. Liquid metal is injected into the die at relatively high speed, and under high pressure. HPDC is a complicated process, and energy intensive, therefore, numerical modelling, analysis and optimization technologies are essential to understand the parameters affecting the process, analyse its performance, and to further select the optimum parameters that will lead to a better use of the material, less scrap rate, and higher efficiency rates.

Keywords

Magnesium, Numerical Analysis, Modelling, Die Casting

INTRODUCTION

The UK/International automotive industry is moving towards using lightweight metals rather than traditional heavier options such as steel in order to improve vehicle fuel efficiency, reduce emissions, and enhance vehicle drivability and performance. The most common material for lightweighting automotive parts is aluminium even though it is more than 50% heavier than another, more overlooked option, magnesium. Other than that, magnesium has similar mechanical properties to aluminium which makes it an auspicious contender in vehicle lightweighting. However at the time of writing magnesium prices are nearly double those of aluminium which is likely to contribute to the lack of uptake of this material because price is a major contributor to most large-scale engineering decisions. At a similar price point, magnesium parts are superior to aluminium ones for the majority of automotive applications. Assuming that raw material costs remain constant for the foreseeable future then the only means of closing the magnesium and aluminium part cost gap would be to optimise the magnesium part manufacturing process.

High Pressure Die Casting (HPDC) is a manufacturing process that is currently used to make magnesium components for the automotive industry. The process involves injecting molten metal into a die at speeds of 30-100m/s, pressures of up to 1200 bar and at temperatures in excess of 600°C. HPDC is an incredibly complex process with many in the industry considering it more of an art than a science. The complexity of HPDC makes it difficult to obtain consistent quality castings, with some manufacturers incurring 25% part rejection rates.

Computational fluid dynamics (CFD) is a tool which is used across many engineering applications to model fluid flow; this highly versatile tool allows for relatively low cost and non-invasive testing/prototyping to be conducted for any fluid flow and heat transfer application. Post-processing of CFD simulations provides users with both quantitative results from data extraction as well as qualitative results through flow visualization. This enables problems to be understood in a technical sense but also that results are easier to communicate to non-specialized audiences.

The specific thermofluidic aspects of a HPDC process are:
- Multiphase flow.
- Convective heat transfer and conduction.
- Significant viscosity change.
- Non-Newtonian flow.
- Phase-change.

The combination of these already complicated thermofluidic processes makes accurate modelling of HPDC challenging and more computationally expensive than single phase, isothermal flows due to the greater number of equations that require solving. In this chapter, the authors will introduce commonly-used CFD simulation methods that are used to model the HPDC process, explain the challenges in simulating these flows and discuss the limitations and abilities of current verification/validation practices.

CFD SIMULATION METHODS:

CFD is not a panacea for the prevention of defects in HPDC. As stated above, CFD has many excellent capabilities such as controlling input parameters, extracting data and visualizing flows which would be impossible to do, or at best unfeasible, experimentally. However numerical modelling has many potential sources of error and inaccuracy. Simulations require assumption of fluid properties/flow behaviour to be made which may have significant effects on the physicality of the results. Numerical modelling can capture filling-related defects, excess of material and thermal contraction defects (Bonollo *et al.,* 2015). CFD can solve for instantaneous flow and thus can capture the nature of transient flow, model heat transfer and deal with phase interactions.

Some issues cannot be captured by CFD such as undesirable phases being present, gas-related defects or whether the part is out of tolerance. However, there is a limit to the size of the flow scale that can be achieved. It cannot determine the microstructure of the cooled metal, nor can it model the small-scale defects. CFD methods are largely used for filling simulations and to determine whether cooling flows exist. It is advantageous that CFD allows users to control the inputs; however, HPDC can be so variable that defining the accurate inputs can be challenging. This section presents an introduction to the Volume of Fluid (VoF), Smoothed Particle Hydrodynamics (SPH), and Lattice-Boltzmann methods (LBM), which are three of the most commonly used CFD methods for HPDC applications.

Volume of Fluid
The VoF approach models the free surface interaction between two, or more, fluids. The method uses both Lagrangian and Eulerian coordinates. It is also understood that in fluid dynamics modelling, any materials interface including those with deformable structures should be modelled as free boundaries. Using Lagrangian coordinates for fluid modelling is considered by dividing the domain into elements that remain identified for the whole solution time. On the contrary, in the Eulerian representation, each element's body and surface should be computed at each time step, in order to compute the flow of the fluid through the mesh (Hirt and Nichols, 1981).

In this respect, the marker particle method is used to track the interface movement and deformation offering accurate results in two-dimensional problems, but it can suffer from the need for huge computational overhead when dealing with three-dimensional problems. Alternatively in VoF, only one value is used for each variable to define the fluid state which results in significantly reduced computational expense and memory requirements. Also, because VoF follows regions rather than surfaces, all problems associated with intersecting surfaces are avoided. As a result, VoF is shown as a flexible and efficient method that can deal with a variety of complicated boundaries Cleary *et al.* (2002). An important feature of VoF methods is that contact angles are imposed geometrically, which means that interface angles are considered as boundary condition which again help to reduce computational needs.

VoF method was used by Mahady *et al.* (2015) to simulate fluid/fluid interfaces with solid boundaries. The model was used to describe the wetting and de-wetting of fluids on substrates characterised by random contact angles. Models were successfully validated by comparing numerical results with the Cox–Voinov law for drop spreading. In other work, VoF approach was used by Saeedipour at al. (2014) to model the global spreading of liquid metal jet in the high pressure die casting, with an Eulerian-Lagrangian framework to track the droplets after formation. Destination has to be calculated very carefully, as wavy destination can result in cold shut defect, while high atomization can increase the porosity. Validation of the numerical modelling was performed using water analogy to capture the flow regime changes and drop formation, with a very good agreement between experimental and numerical results being shown.

An optimization of the HPDC process was conducted by Kong *et al.* (2008). The die temperature profiles were monitored by infrared thermograph technology and the internal cooling system was optimized to provide even cooling to the components and the die. Cooling channels were redesigned to improve the cooling efficiency and reduce the cooling time. It can be seen from (figure 1) that the temperature is higher in the central area of the die compared with the surrounding areas as the heat is trapped and conduction to the cooling pipes is slow. It is evident that the highest temperature with long cycle time, is lower than that with a shorter cycle time.

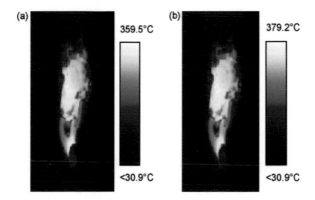

FIGURE 1: Thermal images when die is open (a) with longer cycle time and (b) with shorter cycle time (Kong *et al.*, 2008).

Homayonifar et al. (2008) used novel methods to calculate splash droplet trajectories and regions of 'trapped' air from VoF and single-phase simulations, respectively. The droplet trajectories were calculated using pressure, drag, and gravitational forces once the droplet was 'released' from the free-surface VoF simulations. Locations of air entrapment/porosity were modelled using single-phase CFD simulations. Single-phase simulations lack the capability to capture larger, macro-scale bubbles in a fluid. The mass fraction of air was modelled using a scalar transport equation, which gave the capability to calculate the presence of smaller bubbles in a fluid.

VoF methods are very popular when it comes to modelling metal flow in HPDC. This is mainly due to ease of implementation through commercial software packages such as Magmasoft and Flow-3D (Hirt and Nichols., 1981, Mahady et al., 2015). VoF can be used for simple HPDC approaches but the inclusion of moving parts would be more cumbersome than other approaches due to the requirement for a computational mesh. The stability of VoF is also highly dependent on mesh quality which can become poor at regions of complex geometry.

Smoothed Particle Hydrodynamics
SPH is a Lagrangian-based fluid modelling approach where the positions/velocities of a collection of particles are used to represent bulk fluid movement. SPH is a commonly-used method to simulate HPDC for a number of reasons including the potential speed-up of simulations over conventional finite volume method simulations, the meshless capability which allows for the flow through complex geometry to be simulated, and the implicit conservation of mass, energy and momentum, which aid numerical stability.

When the influence of air is neglected in multiphase simulations, SPH can be considered more efficient than conventional CFD methods because only the particles that represent the denser phase require modelling. Mesh-based CFD methods are able to concentrate meshes in certain areas to reduce computational cost but for spatially varying flows this can be highly inefficient. Adaptive meshes provide an alternative, where meshes are dynamically-refined in 'regions of interest' such as high strain rate. The drawback of dynamic mesh refinement is the computational overhead of 'remaking' the mesh during the simulation process which can be prohibitively expensive. SPH allows engineers and researchers to capture regions of flow interest without wasting computational effort on unnecessary cells or remaking meshes.

For highly-complex geometries mesh-based techniques often produce poor quality meshes and thus inaccurate or unstable simulations. Because SPH is meshless, fluid flow around complicated geometries can be simulated with relative simplicity. There is some evidence to support the fact that 50 times fewer particles than adaptive mesh cells can produce similar results (Liu and Liu, 2003). However, this has not been verified for all applications. The computational overhead of SPH simulations scales with NlogN, where N is the number of particles.

Lattice-Boltzmann Method
The LBM is a non-standard CFD approach which solves the discrete Boltzmann equation using particle collision models to simulate fluid flow. LBM considers the flow on a mesoscopic scale with probability distribution functions being solved to obtain fluid properties. The LBM method has an advantage over other CFD methods in that it was specifically designed to run efficiently on parallel architectures, such as GPUs and hetero- and homogenous supercomputing clusters. This level of efficiency means that complex fluid-flow problems such

as fully resolved multi-phase flow with small droplets and bubbles can be modelled with greater accuracy when using similar resources with Finite Volume Method (FVM) simulations. Practical engineering CFD simulations based on FVM often require highly complex meshes which can take hours, or sometimes days, to produce. The lattices used for LBM are comparatively simpler and are considered to require a much lower fraction of the computational cost.

HPDC MODELLING CHALLENGES

In order to create physically representative simulations, accurate input data is first required. In many cases the inputs to numerical simulations are approximated to make the modelling procedure easier or because they are unknowns. Examples of this are assumptions of uniformity of mass flow rate into the die and die face temperatures. Another challenge is associated with the fact that viscosity is a function of temperature, where the molten metal becomes increasingly viscous as temperature approaches its freezing temperature. Detailed viscosity vs temperature and heat transfer vs temperature information is not always available for all alloys so assumptions of behaviour must be made. Between castings, the HPDC die face is sprayed with a lubricant to prevent the part from 'sticking'. The addition of this lubricant will have some influence on heat transfer between the fluid and the wall, as well as the shear forces on the wall.

VERIFICATION AND VALIDATION

Verification and validation experiments are essential in order to ensure that simulation results are both physical and accurate. In this instance, simulation verification is referred to as the means of ensuring that simulations are 'consistent' i.e. that the results don't change between two similar simulations. In FVM, this is performed using mesh sensitivity studies, where users determine whether an initial mesh has the capability to resolve flow features of importance by using a finer mesh. Mesh refinement is continued until flow properties are comparable between at least two simulations of different mesh densities.

For simulations of HPDC using the VoF approach, mesh sensitivity is used for verification. In SPH simulations, the user increases the number of particles which represent the fluid (or each fluid) and compares the results. If the results of two simulations with different particle numbers are comparable then the particle number can be considered 'consistent'. Once the simulation results have reached this stage, then validation against physical experiments can be performed. A point to note here is that for die filling simulations, the number of particles in a simulation will increase with time because the amount of fluid is increasing. Validation can take a number of forms such as comparing flow variables at specific locations and/or times as in the physical experiments. This approach would be considered as quantitative which means that there are exact values to compare. Quantitative data can be very hard to obtain because of the cost of measurement equipment, potential interference with the flow and potential damage to equipment due to very high temperatures involved in HPDC.

On the other hand, qualitative validation is very popular due to its 'user friendly nature' and often takes the form of comparing flow images at different times during simulation/experiment. Due to the fact that the HPDC dies are made from high-strength, opaque materials, flow visualisation becomes challenging. One alternative is to perform a water filling experiment with a transparent die (Cleary *et al.*, 2010), however fluid viscosity, phase change and heat transfer are all neglected in this method. The second alternative is to perform 'short-shot' castings and simulations (Cleary *et al.*, 2006) which provide a view of the fluid simulations after the event but fail to show the transient behaviour that could be obtained from quantitative methods. In the cases discussed above, only qualitative validation is performed. Qualitative validation allows for easy understanding of the results however it makes quantification of the differences between experiments and simulations very difficult.

CONCLUSIONS

In this chapter, it has been explained that it is advantageous to use CFD to understand, analyse, and further optimize the HPDC process. The common CFD methods that are used to model the process were listed and explained. Furthermore, the challenges that are facing the numerical modelling of this complicated process were mentioned, while methods used for the verification and validation of the developed models were summarized.

References

Bonollo, F., Gramegna, N. and Timelli, G., 2015. High-pressure die-casting: Contradictions and challenges. Jom, 67(5), pp.901-908.

Cleary, P., Ha, J., Alguine, V., Nguyen, T., 2002. Flow modelling in casting processes. Applied Mathematical Modelling, 26(2), pp. -190.

Cleary, P., Ha, J., Prakash, M., Nguyen, T., 2006. 3D SPH flow predictions and validation for high pressure die casting of automotive components. Applied Mathematical Modelling, 30(11), pp.1406-1427.

Hirt, C., W., and Nichols, B., D., 1981. Volume of fluid (VOF) method for the dynamics of free boundaries. Journal of computational physics, 39(1), pp.201-225.

Homayonifar, P., Babaei, R., Attar, E., Shahinfar, S., Davami, P., 2008. Numerical modeling of splashing and air entrapment in high-pressure die casting. The International Journal of Advanced Manufacturing Technology, 39(3-4), pp.219-228.

Kong, L., X., She, F., H., Gao, W., M., Nahavandi, S., Hodgson, P., D., 2008. Integrated optimization system for high pressure die casting processes. Journal of materials processing technology, 201(1-3), pp.629-634.

Liu, G.R. and Liu, M.B., 2003. Smoothed particle hydrodynamics: a meshfree particle method. World Scientific, Singapore.

Mahady, K., Afkhami, S., Kondic, L., 2015. A volume of fluid method for simulating fluid/fluid interfaces in contact with solid boundaries. Journal of Computational Physics, 294, pp.243-257.

Saeedipour, M., Schneiderbauer, S., Pirker, S., Bozorgi, S., 2014. A numerical and experimental study of flow behaviour in high pressure die casting. Magnesium Technology 2014. Edited by: Martyn Alderman, Michele V. Manuel, Norbert Hort, and Neale R. Neelameggham TMS (The Minerals, Metals & Materials Society), 2014.

Final Thoughts: Reflections & Conclusions

Adel Aneiba, Hanifa Shah and Cham Athwal

School of Computing & Digital Technology, Birmingham City University,
Millennium Point, Birmingham, UK. B4 7XG.
Email :{Adel.Aneiba,Hanifa.Shah,Cham.Athwal}@bcu.ac.uk

The book has been produced as a result of long term relationships with several partners within industry through robust collaboration programmes such as the exclusive partnership between Birmingham City University and Meridian Lightweight Technologies UK – the world's largest producer of magnesium die cast components. Since forming in 2016, with a group visit to the factory, the strategic alliance has seen the two organisations work together in education, research and development of magnesium use and now, how digital technologies can push business growth through increased productivity and sustainability within its core using Industry 4.0 technologies. Further, the partnership, also builds on the heritage of Birmingham City University as a catalyst for growth among regional industries through both knowledge transfer and by offering a unique, interdisciplinary approach.

From a strategic perspective, BCU and through the Faculty of Computing, Engineering and Built Environment seeks to identify new ways to offer more sustainable products, services and business models for manufacturers and their potential clients. This book looks to highlight the potential of Industry 4.0, by showcasing it as a viable alternative for the manufacturing sector, including the automotive industry. The strength of the book lies in its levels of collaboration and partnership which spans both academic and professional staff, and the undergraduate and post-graduate student body of Birmingham City University. Strategically, the project aligns with Birmingham City University's institutional commitment to STEAM-based learning (STEM with Arts-based subjects).

STEAM is designed to drive an increasingly enterprise-focussed education, developing employability and entrepreneurship skills. The challenges set by Industrial partners clearly demonstrate how arts and creativity can be combined with STEAM subjects to drive innovation, skills, research and economic growth and facilitate innovative solutions to new business ideas, products and services. The purpose of the book is to explore the importance of industry 4.0 as a digital enabler for the manufacturing sector – showcasing it as a strategic move, especially for car manufacturers and the aerospace industry in terms of productivity, business growth and sustainability. This book represents a welcome enhancement to our teaching and learning, and will serve to capture creative and innovative practice that can be shared across the industry community.

Birmingham City University is the **University 'for' Birmingham.** We strive to realise our vision to transform the region by accelerating business growth and employability within the local economy. This can be achieved by delivering: practise-based research and knowledge transfer, business growth expertise and support activities, a highly-skilled, work-ready graduate workforce and interdisciplinary academic and industry collaborations. BCU and through its business enabler arms such as 'The Institute for Sustainable Futures (iSF)', will connect businesses and organisations with Birmingham City University's academic experts and specialists to help them drive unique practise-based research, new knowledge and innovative solutions to their real-world business or societal challenges.

BCU academic experts support regional SMEs and businesses by creating and delivering a portfolio of business growth activities from one to one business analysis and consultancy to workshops, knowledge transfer partnerships and higher and degree apprentices. In addition, they work with regional SME leaders to identify the skills their businesses need to achieve their growth objectives and deliver bespoke skills solutions that match their business needs to highly-skilled work-ready graduates and/or employee up-skilling and training opportunities.

STEAMhouse is BCU's new centre aimed at encouraging the collaboration of the arts, science, technology, engineering and maths (STEAM) sectors. Interdisciplinary collaborations at STEAMhouse help entrepreneurs, SMEs and organisations with strong business ideas but a lack of knowledge, skills or resources to 'plan it, make it and commercialise it'. More than a makerspace, STEAMhouse is a melting pot of technology, facilities, expert knowledge and specialist skills that put the Arts into STEM to drive business innovation and regional growth.

Partnership with local and global organisations in order to develop cutting-edge expertise is at the heart of our approach to making our teaching and research vital to the evolving market for digital and technical skills. BCU research has developed technologies and solutions in a number of areas including digital media, data analytics, cybersecurity, wireless sensor networks and engineering which are being applied in Smart Cities, Digital Health, Digital Productivity, Creative Industries and Advanced Manufacturing (Industry 4.0).

We at BCU are committed to transferring the expertise, technology and skills that our research and innovative practice has helped us to develop, to external organisations with the aim of embedding new innovation and skills to improve our partners' performance. We work with our partner organizations to enable them to drive innovation and new business ideas to sharpen their competitive edge. With our help they can get the additional skills and knowledge required to help with business growth.

FIGURE 1: Birmingham City University Academic Team and The Institute of Sustainable Futures (iSF) visit to Meridian Lightweight Technologies UK for the official launch of the project in April 2018

Cham Athwal is Birmingham City University's Professor of Digital Technology and heads its Digital Media Technology (DMT) Lab. With a PhD in Physics, Cham was firstly employed in high technology R&D at CERN and GEC Ltd. Then as an academic for nearly 30 years, he has been continuously working in the co-creation and application of multimedia and digital technologies to address the problems of numerous industrial and commercial organisations especially in the automotive, jewellery and wider manufacturing and creative industries.

Hanifa Shah is Executive Dean and Professor of Information Systems in the Faculty of Computing, Engineering and the Built Environment at Birmingham City University. She has been successful in securing significant amounts of funding for projects from industry and research councils. Her research interests and PhD supervisions include information systems and their development, knowledge management, enterprise architectures & enterprise systems, business process change and smart cities, IT professional development & research methods and qualifications through work-based learning.

Professor Gareth Neighbour joined BCU as Head of School of Engineering and the Built Environment in October 2016 from Oxford Brookes where he was the Head of Mechanical Engineering and Mathematical Sciences. He joined Brookes in 2011 from Hull where he had formed the Materials and Process Performance Group. Previously he led the internationally recognised Bath Nuclear Materials Group. To date he has provided independent research and advice to the nuclear and other heavy industries including the regulator and also the IAEA in Vienna. Research income to date is ~£3 million. Prior to his academic career, during 1992-1996, Gareth worked for AEA Technology at their Windscale plant where, amongst other things, he managed the integration of various engineering systems. A significant proportion of Gareth's research is interdisciplinary in nature. His interest ranges from integrated management systems to fracture mechanics and fundamental structure-property relationships of engineering materials. Currently the main thrust is the effectiveness of UK gas-cooled nuclear reactor core designs, particularly materials performance and the functionality of core components to support life extension using various modelling and analytical techniques. Other research interests include nuclear energy and graphite technology in general, post irradiation evaluation of nuclear materials (inc. fuels), carbon deposition, mechanical properties of porous materials, redundancy in design, BPEO and HAZOP studies. He also has interests in systems theory & waste materials treatment related to design theory and the effect of risk assessment methodology has on environmental and societal decision-making. He is passionate about employer facing education and has extensive experience of programme development including various grants from HEFCE. In his spare time, he enjoys family life, F1 and genealogy.

Professor Andy Aftelak is the Head of the School, Computing and Digital Technology at Birmingham City University. He is an experienced engineer and senior executive with 26 years of service in industrial research and advanced product technology. He holds 24 patents and has been an active participant in international standards bodies and forums, as well as being a fellow of the IET and a member of both the IEEE and the SCTE. His knowledge of software development tools and processes, among others, stems from a series of technical leadership positions with Motorola, including Director of the UK research lab and Vice-President of Research at Motorola Mobility. Andy's last role in industry was vice-president and director of

ARRIS's Applied Research Centre, where he led the team that creates new products and services for the cable and IP TV industry.

Mohamed Gaber is a Professor in Data Analytics at the School of Computing and Digital Technology, Birmingham City University. Mohamed received his PhD from Monash University, Australia. He has published over 150 papers, co-authored 3 monograph-style books, and edited/co-edited 6 books on data mining and knowledge discovery. His work has attracted close to four thousand citations, with an h-index of 32. Mohamed has served in the programme committees of major conferences related to data mining, including ICDM, PAKDD, ECML/PKDD and ICML. He has also co-chaired numerous scientific events on various data mining topics. In 2016, Mohamed was the programme committee co-chair of the 17th IEEE International Conference on Mobile Data Management.

Professor Josephs, Chartered Fellow of the British Computer Society, has a BSc (Hons) degree in Mathematics from University College London and MSc and DPhil degrees in Computer Science from the University of Oxford. After spending a year as a Visiting Scientist at IBM Yorktown Heights in 1987, he returned to Oxford where he was appointed a member of the Faculty of Mathematical Sciences and a lecturer at Trinity College. He joined London South Bank University in 1993 and was promoted to Professor of Computing in 1998. Between 1992 and 2006, he engaged with the Microelectronics Industry as the leader of an inter-organizational expert community of practice that was supported by the European Commission. He was appointed a Senior Fellow in Cyber Security at the University of Warwick, 2010-2012, and Professor of Computer Science at Birmingham City University in 2015. He has served as a member of the UK Computing Research Committee since 2004, the Engineering and Physical Sciences Research Council's Peer Review College since 2010 and the Information Assurance Advisory Council's Academic Liaison Panel since 2012.

Mak Sharma has an international reputation for his extensive work on the use of Vendor Resources and embedding these into various qualifications. He has worked to engage with 10 of largest IT companies such as such as Cisco, Microsoft, SAS, Oracle etc. to provide a rich set of problem based learning throughout computing, communications and engineering courses. Whilst Head of School, he provided leadership and strategic direction for a business worth in excess of £10m across the Computing and Electronics Communications disciplines, through contract fulfilment, research and high quality academic delivery. Specifically Mak managed the development and delivery across 11 courses such as Computer Science and Computer Games Technology that included content such as such as Game Engine Programming, Human Computer Interaction, Artificial Intelligence. This success of this work was recognised in 2017, when Mak was appointed Professor in Computer Science Education. Over the last 5 years, based on the technologies used on these courses Mak led the development and delivery of 12 contracts valued over a £1m. He now spends his time leading the Cloud Computing Centre to deliver courses in Computer Networks & Security and Cloud Computing related modules. He has been instrumental in leading the developments of content for modules such as Cloud Infrastructure and Services, Infrastructure Storage and Management, Software Defined Networks and Intelligent Sensor Systems. Mak is the also the course Leader for the MSc Data Networks & Security; and his lecturing is in Networking, IoT & Intelligent Sensor Systems. Mak's research interests are: Computer Science Education, Industrial Engagement, and Employability, Software Defined Networks and Cloud based Decision Support Systems.

Professor Oraifige joined BCU as Head of Engineering Centre in November 2016 from University of Derby where he was the Deputy Head of Department of Engineering. He is qualified chartered engineer and a fellow member of the Institution of Mechanical Engineers (FIMechE). His current role involves continuous engagement with industry in many ways including R&D, development of new courses, short courses, consultancy, KTPs, etc. His research work involves Knowledge Based Engineering, virtual reality and finite element analysis. The research work investigates and develops tools to facilitate the integration of such technologies and hence providing real time design analysis capabilities in virtual environment. His other research work includes: Process Flow and Shop floor Layout Optimisation; Production planning and scheduling; Production / Manufacturing Engineering; New Product Development; Stress Analysis and Design Optimisation and Engineering Design and Simulation. Professor's Oraifige Research Track Record Includes: Assistant Editor for the International Journal of Engineering Simulation (www.intJES.co.uk); Organiser of the 2007 International Conference on Modelling, Simulation & Visualisation Methods at the WORLDCOMP'07, Las Vegas; Number of PhD and MPhil Completion; Number of Peer Reviewed Journal Papers and industrial reports and Successful external funding (KTPs, etc.) in excess of £1 M.

Wenyan Wu is a Professor in Smart Sensor and Advanced System Engineering, School of Engineering and the Built Environment, Birmingham City University. She has research expertise in sensor technology, smart sensing and sensor network, signal processing, sensor fusion and intelligent monitoring, modelling and optimisation, digital technology and extended to Internet of Things technology (IoTs) and currently she is leading a research project *IoT4Win-Internet of Thing for Smart Water Innovative Networks* funded by H2020-MSCA-ITN. She has completed many research projects funded from EPSRC, Horizon2020, EU-FP7, Innovate UK, European Next Generation Infrastructure Foundation, The Royal Society and industries.

Professor Stephen Brown has over 25 years' experience in both extrusion and high pressure die casting of Magnesium in both the nuclear and automotive industries, and has been with Meridian as its first UK employee since July 1999. Returned to the UK to take on the role as Product Development Engineer at Meridian after working in New Zealand as Operations Manager for an aluminium die casting Company, and played a pivotal role in starting up the Meridian UK operations in Sutton in Ashfield. He was originally based in Warwick at Meridian offices set up to serve the customer with products manufactured out of our Italian operations, and progressed to take on the Business Development Manager of our European Operations before moving to Sutton in Ashfield after the factory start up in 2003. Stephen was responsible for many Magnesium projects introducing structures into various vehicles and models across numerous OEMs, the most recent of which being the highly successful Daimler Chrysler Mercedes compact SUV, and continues to work with them throughout its production, supporting in any way possible. Stephen has a passion for Magnesium and has campaigned for industry and engineers to have a better understanding of the material so its many advantages can be utilised and allow it to take its rightful place alongside other structural materials in use today.

Dr Jamil Ahmed has over 25 years of industrial experience with Rover group, BMW and Aston Martin. Jamil is currently Director of Facilities management at Aston Martin, which has involved heading up the construction of a new state of the art production facility in Wales along with total responsibility of all other Aston Martins assets / facilities. In 2017 BCU recognised his services to the automotive industry by awarding him the accolade of 'Doctor of the University'.

Martin Tauber has over 25 years' experience in different raw material related industries, whereas Magnesium has been the most significant one, with executive positions with leading industry players like Hydro Magnesium and Magontec. In, 2009, he founded FAURIS Management, a consulting company which provides services to the Magnesium industry on a global base. Martin is also European Committee Chairman of the International Magnesium Association (IMA) and President of the Critical Raw Material Alliance (CRM).

Makhan Singh has over 25 years automotive experience, having worked for major blue chip automotive organisations such as Jaguar Land Rover, BMW, Johnson Controls and Britax Seating. Also a highly experienced psychotherapist with 20 years of private practice experience and an emotional nerve intelligence (ENI) trainer, Makhan was recently the Programme Manager at Meridian Lightweight Technologies working on the product launch for the Jaguar XE magnesium Front End Carrier and now works as the Development Manager for the Institute for Sustainable Futures at Birmingham City University.

Dr Ian Williams is an Associate Professor in Birmingham City University's DMT Lab. He is an expert in image analysis, Mixed and Augmented Reality (MR/AR), 3D image processing and user interaction. Dr Williams delivers internationally recognised research leading the Image and Mixed Reality group within the DMT Lab. Dr Williams currently acts on the scientific and technical committee for the IEEE ISMAR conference and is a reviewer for several international conferences and journals.

Dr Adel Aneiba is an associate professor at Birmingham City University in the area of computer networks and Internet of Things (IoT). He completed his PhD, in the field of Mobile Computing and Distributed systems, in 2008 from Staffordshire University. He worked for 10 years as a senior ICT consultant for international organisations include UNESCO and several governmental organisations for many years and participated in managing mega ICT projects mainly on data centre designing and development, and reengineering business processes. His current research interests are: IoT; computer networks, evaluation and optimisation; and blockchain. Adel is co-leading several IoT research projects in partnership with West Midlands Combined Authority, Recently, he was awarded innovative UK-Nesta project on using drones in future cities. In addition, He participates in Digital Catapult innovation programme on waste management and air-quality challenges that facing local authorities. Adel is BCU-IBM academic coordinator who is maintaining the relationship on various academic activities include R&D around IoT and BlockChain.

Alan Pendry is an Associate Professor in the University's Centre for Engineering. He is a Fellow of the Higher Education Academy, an Affiliate of the Institution of Engineering Designers and a Member of the Institution of Engineering and Technology (currently pursuing CEng status). He also represents the University on the European Committee of the International Magnesium Association. Approaching his 25th year as an academic, Alan is currently Programme Leader for MEng/BEng Manufacturing Engineering courses and lectures in Engineering Design, Design Management, Quality Management, Project Management and Professional Practice. He has a keen interest in ethics and professionalism and is passionate about climate change mitigation. Working closely with industry to improve manufacturing systems, processes and productivity, Alan's specific interests include vehicle light-weighting and the use of magnesium alloys. Past research includes Hydrogen Fuel Cell Power Systems. Notable achievements to date include development of H2 PEM-FC powertrain for a new generation Tuk-Tuk for the Indian Government, and design and build of H2 PEM-FC powered motorcycle (for the sheer fun of it!).

Dr Abed Alaswad is a Senior Lecturer in Engineering Design. During his career, he worked on different research projects in Dublin City University, the University of the West of Scotland and Birmingham City University. Abed has published his research findings through his academic career in more than 40 articles in high impact factor journals and international conferences. He is a member of the International Magnesium Association and is currently supervising two PhD students in Wind mapping (Newton Fund) and Microalgae cultivation.

Dr.Shadi Basurra is a Senior Lecturer in Computer Science at Birmingham City University, UK. Shadi received his Bsc (Hons) in Computer Science from Exeter University, UK, and MSc in Distributed Systems and Networks from Kent University at Canterbury, UK. He obtained his PhD from the University of Bath in collaboration with Bristol University, UK. After his PhD, Shadi worked at Sony, developing Goal Decision Systems. He was awarded The Yemen President National Science Prize (2010), Best Presentation at Meeting of Minds – Bath 2012, MEX Scholarship 2013, (PhD Scholarship from Toshiba ltd, Great Western Research and Yemen gov. - 2009) and various academic grants. Shadi's research interests include multi-agent systems, game theory, multi-objective optimisation, machine learning in IoT, energy efficiency in smart buildings, emulation of mobile ad hoc networks and nature inspired computing. He has published a number of peer-reviewed scientific articles at international conferences and journals, and has taught postgraduate and undergraduate courses in computer science and networking.

Dr Roger Tait is an experienced software engineer with more than 15 years of service in academic research environments. He completed his PhD, in the field of Parallel Architectures, in 2007 at Nottingham Trent University. After graduating he joined the Centre of Innovation and Technology Exploitation at Nottingham Trent University as a research fellow developing mobile applications and web services. In 2008 he joined the University of Cambridge Behavioural and Clinical Neuroscience Institute to provide technical consultancy for parallel processing within small and large scale architectures. He is currently a lecturer in Distributed Computing at Birmingham City University.

Dr.Vitor Jesus is a Lecturer with Birmingham City University and has 20 years of professional experience, split between Industry and Academia. He holds a BSc in Physics, a MSc and PhD in Computer Science and Networks and industry certifications in Cyber Security and Data Privacy. He has 20 years of professional experience, split between Industry and Academia. He has held positions with different companies, from start-ups to large and well-known organisations. He has authored a number of papers, has been in the review panel of several conferences, was a visiting scholar in different institutions, such as Carnegie Mellon University, and has worked in a number of international projects. His current research and teaching interests are in CyberSecurity and Privacy. We live in a world where CyberSecurity is becoming a basic need just like physical safety is; or its absence can bring down a business, a community or a country. We are also moving towards a world where there is no Privacy by default and everyone's Identity and Data will eventually be stolen. Vitor's research aims at bringing control back to users by looking at technologies and solutions, such as Blockchains, Secure Networks or Artificial Intelligence, whether it is in Cars, the Internet, Medical devices, Enterprises, Factories or Cities.

Dr Gerald Feldman is a lecturer in Information Systems at Birmingham City University, in the School of Computing and Digital Technology. He research and teaching interests include Technology adoption, Business Process Change and Enterprise systems. Gerald has over six years' industrial experience in managing, designing and implementing information systems. His current research focuses on technological change, with the purpose of shifting our thinking away from the deterministic technology-centred perception to a people-centred information-led perspective ensuring technical, social, environmental and organisational aspects of a system are considered together to deliver better value to organisations.

Dr Dominic Flynn is a lecturer in mechanical engineering at Birmingham City University. His specialism is modelling fluid flows with computational fluid dynamics which he developed while conducting a PhD and Post-Doc at the University of Birmingham. Dominic has an international network of research contacts and his work has led him to consult for several companies such as network Rail and SNC-Lavalin (formerly Interfleet).

Dr. Mariam Adedoyin-Olowe is an Assistant Lecturer in Big Data Analytics and Statistical Techniques in the Expert System Group of the School of Computing Science and Digital Technology (CDT) of Birmingham City University, United Kingdom. She obtained a PhD degree in Computing Science from the School of Computing Science and Digital Media (IDEAS Research Institute) of Robert Gordon University (RGU), United Kingdom in 2015. Her research applied Association Rule Mining to Twitter data to detect and track topic/event from real life occurrences for information and decision making. She currently teaches Post Graduate modules in CDT and also conduct academic research in the field of Computing Science. Mariam's research interest includes: Data Analytics, Data Mining, Social Media Analytics, Topic Detection and Tracking, Sentiment Analysis and Text Mining.

Dr Maite Frutos-Pascual is a Research Fellow in Birmingham City University's DMT Lab. Her expertise ranges a variety of different topics in Augmented and Virtual Reality (AR, VR), HCI, intelligent systems, data analysis and retrieval using different sensors (i.e. eye trackers, depth sensors, biofeedback), usability and user interaction analysis. Dr Frutos-Pascual delivers internationally recognised research with her work being published in leading international journals and conferences. She acts as a reviewer for several international conferences and journals.

Dr Vahid Javidroozi is currently a 'Research Fellow in Smart City Systems Engineering' at Birmingham City University (BCU), working on several research projects mainly in the domain of smart cities, systems engineering, enterprise systems integration, and process change. Vahid obtained BSc Computer Science in 2009. He also acquired his MSc Enterprise Systems Management with distinction in May 2012. Vahid has also awarded SAP ERP associate consultant certificate and currently working as an SAP ERP trainer in BCU. In addition, he occasionally works as a guest lecturer. He is also a committee member of international conference and journal on smart systems, devices, and technologies.

Author Index

Subject Index (by Keywords)

NOTES